D0347413

CGP
– books like no others!

CGP

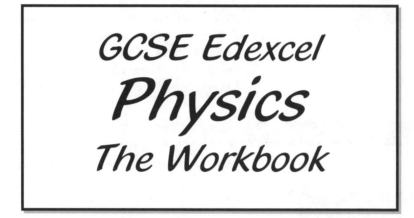

GCSE Edexcel
Physics
The Workbook

This book is for anyone doing **GCSE Edexcel Physics**.

It's full of **tricky questions**... each one designed to make you **sweat**
— because that's the only way you'll get any **better**.

There are questions to see **what facts** you know. There are questions
to see how well you can **apply those facts**. And there are questions
to see what you know about **how science works**.

It's also got some daft bits in to try and make the whole
experience at least vaguely entertaining for you.

What CGP is all about

Our sole aim here at CGP is to produce the highest
quality books — carefully written, immaculately presented
and dangerously close to being funny.

Then we work our socks off to get them
out to you — at the cheapest possible prices.

Contents

Published by CGP

Editors:
Helena Hayes, Felicity Inkpen, Julie Wakeling, Sarah Williams.

Contributors:
Steve Coggins, Mark A Edwards, Paddy Gannon, Dr Giles R Greenway,
Frederick Langridge, Barbara Mascetti, Pat Szczesniak, Jim Wilson.

ISBN: 978 1 84762 631 8

With thanks to Catherine Davis, Karen Wells and Dawn Wright for the proofreading.

Pages 63, 89, 90, 91, 103 and 116 contain public sector information published by the Health
and Safety Executive and licensed under the Open Government Licence v1.0.

Groovy website: www.cgpbooks.co.uk

Printed by Elanders Ltd, Newcastle upon Tyne.
Jolly bits of clipart from CorelDRAW®

Based on the classic CGP style created by Richard Parsons.

Changing Ideas About the Solar System

Q1 a) Tick the boxes to show whether the sentences are true or false.

True **False**

   i) Waves can be used to find out information about the Universe. ☐ ☐

   ii) We can observe stars and planets because they both give out visible light. ☐ ☐

   iii) Telescopes are our only method of observing visible light from the Universe. ☐ ☐

   iv) The invention of the telescope helped increase our knowledge
of our Solar System. ☐ ☐

b) Write a correction for each false sentence.

....

....

....

Q2 Match up the descriptions with the correct method of observing the Universe.
Each description might match more than one method.

Only really useful for mapping positions, e.g. of stars

Earth-based telescopes

Can be used to magnify images

Allow distant objects to be seen in more detail

Naked-eye observations

Observations can be made more difficult by
light pollution and the Earth's atmosphere

Q3 Give **three advantages** of using **photography** to observe the Universe,
compared with using telescopes or the naked eye.

1. ....

2. ....

3. ....

Q4 Describe the main features of the **geocentric model** of the
Solar System. Include a sketch of the model in your answer.

....

....

....

Changing Ideas About the Solar System

Q5 Our ideas about the structure of the Solar System have changed over time.

a) Complete the following sentences.

> **i)** The heliocentric model states that all the .... orbit
>
> the ....
>
> **ii)** The orbits in the heliocentric model are all perfect ....
>
> **iii)** In the heliocentric model the .... is at the centre of the Universe.

b) Give **one** difference between our current model of the Solar System and the heliocentric model.

....

....

c) Briefly describe how telescopes in general have helped change our ideas about the Solar System.

....

....

....

....

An egocentric model.

Q6 Galileo made some observations of Jupiter using a telescope that helped to provide evidence for the heliocentric model of the Solar System.

a) Briefly describe what Galileo saw when making his observations of Jupiter.

....

....

....

b) Explain how Galileo's observations helped provide evidence to disprove the geocentric model.

....

....

....

....

Waves — Basic Principles

Q1 Complete the sentence using the words given below. You will not have to use all the words.

matter   all   frequency   some   energy

.... waves transfer .... and information

without transferring ....

Q2 Here are **two ways** in which you can make waves on a **slinky** spring.

① ②

Which diagram shows a **transverse** wave, and which one shows a **longitudinal** wave?

Transverse: ....   Longitudinal: ....

Q3 Sort the waves below into two groups — **longitudinal** waves and **transverse** waves.

sunlight   'push-pull' wave on a slinky   S-waves   'shake' wave on a slinky

ultrasound   P-waves   electromagnetic (EM)   birdsong   drumbeat

Longitudinal: ....

....

Transverse: ....

....

Q4 Diagrams A, B and C represent **electromagnetic waves**.

A   B   C

a) Which two diagrams show waves with the same **frequency**?   ...... and ......

b) Which two diagrams show waves with the same **amplitude**?   ...... and ......

c) Which two diagrams show waves with the same **wavelength**?   ...... and ......

Waves — Basic Principles

Q5 The crest of a wave travels 12 m in 5 seconds. Calculate the **speed** of the wave.

....

....

Q6 A ripple in a pond travels at **0.5 m/s**. It makes a duck bob up and down **twice every second**.

a) What is the **frequency** of the duck's bobbing? ....

b) When the duck is on the crest of a wave, **how far away** is the next crest?

Remember what's meant by a wavelength, then use $v = f \times \lambda$.

....

Q7 **Green light** travels at 3×10^8 m/s and has a wavelength of about 5×10^{-7} m.

Calculate the **frequency** of green light. Give the correct unit in your answer.

You'll have to use $v = f \times \lambda$.

....

....

Q8 The graph on the right is a representation of a **sound wave**.

a) What is the **amplitude** of the wave shown by the graph?

....

2 cm
1 cm
0
1 cm
2 cm

0.01 0.02 0.03 time in seconds

b) How many **complete** vibrations are shown? ....

c) **How long** does it take to make each vibration? ....

Q9 Sound waves are **longitudinal** waves.

a) Which **direction** are the vibrations in a longitudinal wave, compared to the direction the wave is **travelling**? ....

b) What is meant by the **frequency** of a longitudinal / sound wave?

....

> **Top Tips:** Woah, those last couple of pages were a bonanza of wave questions. As per usual, it's all really important stuff. Make sure you're happy with what is meant by the frequency, wavelength, amplitude and speed of a wave. And know how to rearrange and use the wave speed equations too.

Reflection and Refraction

Q1 Harriet spends at least an hour looking at herself in a **mirror** every day.
The image she sees is formed from light reflected by the mirror.

a) What is meant by a "normal" when talking about reflection?

....

....

b) Complete the diagram to show an incident
ray of light being reflected by the mirror.
Label the **angle of incidence ,i**, the **normal**,
and the **angle of reflection, r**.

Mirror

Q2 What causes **light** to be **refracted**? Tick the correct box.

☐ Refraction is caused by an image being formed at the boundary between two media.

☐ Refraction is caused by light being reflected off the boundary between two media.

☐ Refraction is caused by one medium being better able to absorb light than another.

☐ Refraction is caused by light changing speed as it enters another medium.

Q3 Jo is looking at a pebble lying on the bottom of a **pool**.

a) Does the bottom of the pool appear to be **nearer** to Jo
or **further away** from her than it actually is?

....

b) Does light travel **faster** or **more slowly** in air than in water?

....

Q4 The diagram shows a light ray
passing through **air** and through **glass**.

medium 1

medium 2

a) Fill in the gaps in this sentence to say
which medium is **air** and which is **glass**.

Medium 1 in the diagram is .... and **medium 2** is ....

b) **Explain** your answer to part **a)**.

....

....

6

<u>Lenses</u>

Q1 Converging lenses are used to focus light.

    a) In the following sentences the words **parallel**, **converging**, **focal point** and **incident** have been replaced by the letters **W**, **X**, **Y**, **Z**. Write down which words are represented by **W**, **X**, **Y** and **Z**.

> *A(n)* **W** *ray passing through the centre of a* **X** *lens from any angle carries on in the same direction.*
>
> *A* **X** *lens causes all* **W** *rays* **Y** *to the axis to meet at the* **Z**.

    W .... X .... Y .... Z ....

    b) Which of the following incident rays do not have their direction changed by a lens?
Tick any boxes which apply.

      ☐ Any ray parallel to the axis   ☐ Any ray passing through the centre of the lens

      ☐ Any ray passing along the axis   ☐ Any ray passing through the focal point

Q2 Some of this diagram has been hidden. Draw in the rest of the diagram, showing the position of the **object** that produced the image you see.

Q3 Briefly describe an **experiment** which could be used to work out the **focal length** of a lens. You may include a sketch in your answer.

....

....

....

Lenses

Q4 Gavin is carrying out an experiment to investigate the factors that affect the **magnification** of a converging lens. He wants to find out how an object's **distance from the lens** affects the image he sees.

a) Briefly describe how he could carry out this investigation.
Your description should include all the equipment he should use.

....

....

....

....

....

....

The results from Gavin's experiment are shown in the table below, where F is the focal point of the lens.

Distance from lens to object	Distance from lens to image	Type of image	Size of image
Greater than 2F	Between 2F and F	Real, inverted	Smaller than object
Equal to 2F		Real, inverted	
Between 2F and F	Greater than 2F		
Less than F	Greater than 2F		Larger than object

b) Fill in the blanks in the table.

c) An object has a height of 1 cm. It stands on the axis of a converging lens, 5 cm away from it. The focal length of the lens (distance from the lens to the focal point) is 2.5 cm.

i) What size will the image be?

....

ii) Where will the image be formed, relative to the lens and the object?

....

Top Tips: In the exam, you might have to **describe** how to carry out a particular experiment. This means you'll have to list the **apparatus** needed and write a **detailed method** for the investigation. Make sure you list every little thing you might need — the examiners aren't mind readers. You might be expected to say what results you'd find too — but don't panic, it'll all be about stuff you've learnt. Yay.

8

Simple and Reflecting Telescopes

Q1 The following ray diagram shows light rays from an object in space entering a **simple telescope**.

a) Complete the diagram by labelling:
   i) where a **real image** will be formed,   **ii)** the **eyepiece** lens.

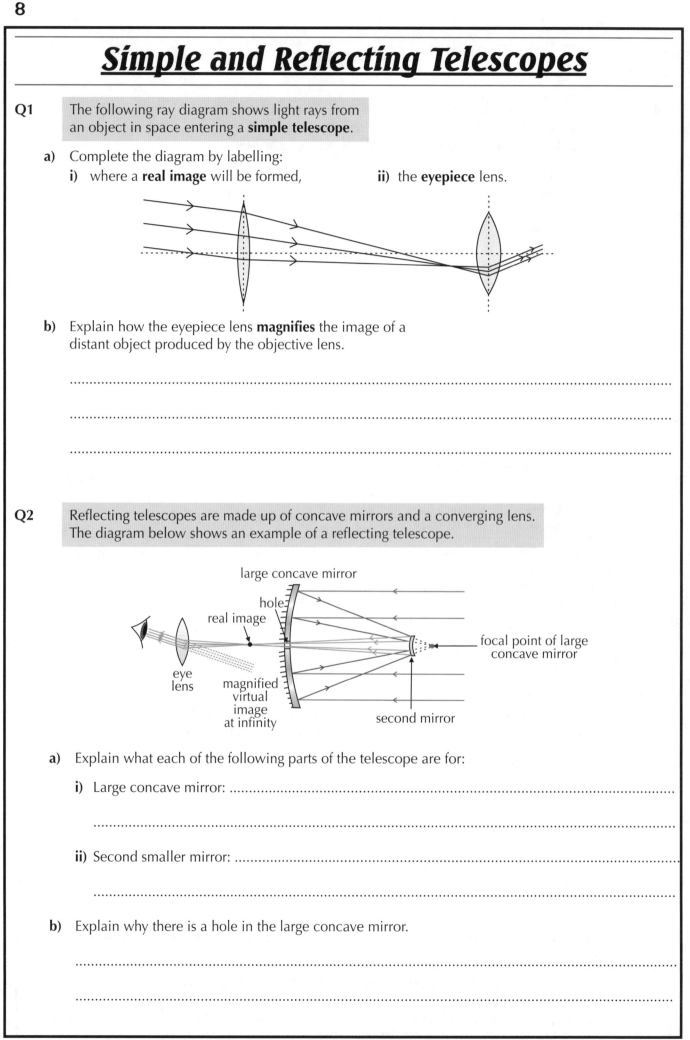

b) Explain how the eyepiece lens **magnifies** the image of a distant object produced by the objective lens.

....

....

....

Q2 Reflecting telescopes are made up of concave mirrors and a converging lens. The diagram below shows an example of a reflecting telescope.

a) Explain what each of the following parts of the telescope are for:

   i) Large concave mirror: ....

   ....

   ii) Second smaller mirror: ....

   ....

b) Explain why there is a hole in the large concave mirror.

....

....

Electromagnetic Waves

Q1   Tick the boxes to show whether the following statements are **true** or **false**.

True False

a)   All EM waves are transverse waves.   ☐ ☐

b)   Radio waves have the shortest wavelength of all EM waves.   ☐ ☐

c)   All EM waves can travel through space.   ☐ ☐

Q2   The table below shows the different possible wavelengths of EM radiation.

Complete the table to show the seven types of EM waves:

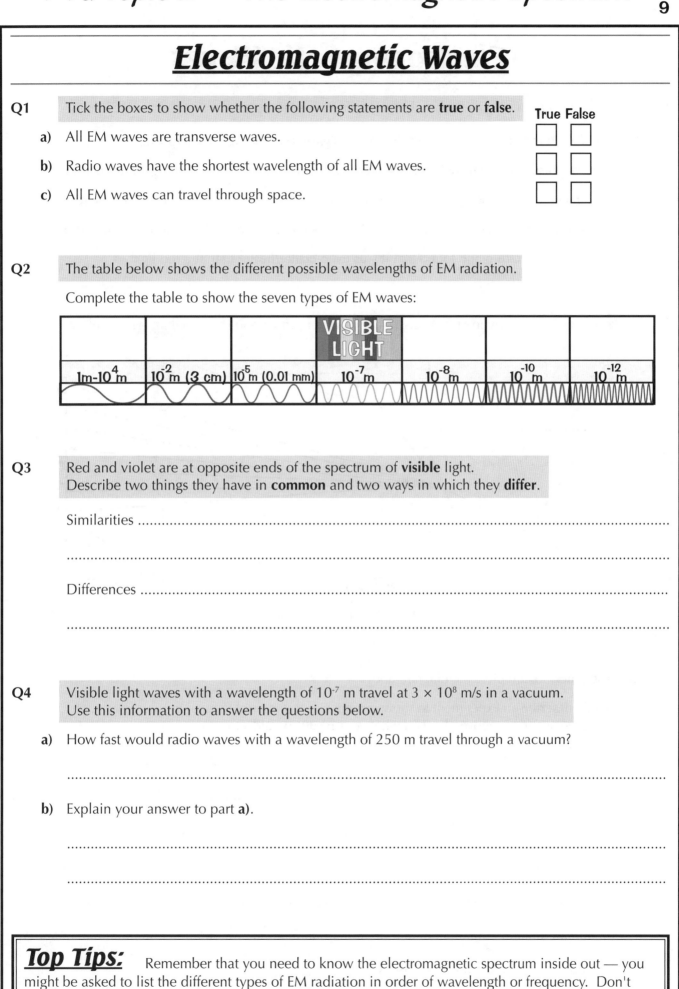

			VISIBLE LIGHT			
$1m-10^4\,m$	$10^{-2}\,m$ (3 cm)	$10^{-5}\,m$ (0.01 mm)	$10^{-7}\,m$	$10^{-8}\,m$	$10^{-10}\,m$	$10^{-12}\,m$

Q3   Red and violet are at opposite ends of the spectrum of **visible** light.
Describe two things they have in **common** and two ways in which they **differ**.

Similarities ....

....

Differences ....

....

Q4   Visible light waves with a wavelength of 10^{-7} m travel at 3×10^8 m/s in a vacuum.
Use this information to answer the questions below.

a)   How fast would radio waves with a wavelength of 250 m travel through a vacuum?

....

b)   Explain your answer to part **a)**.

....

....

Top Tips: Remember that you need to know the electromagnetic spectrum inside out — you might be asked to list the different types of EM radiation in order of wavelength or frequency. Don't forget that all the different radiations form a continuous spectrum — very high frequency radio waves aren't really very different from very low frequency microwaves.

Electromagnetic Waves

Q5   Circle the correct words to complete the following sentences.

While carrying out an experiment shining **sunlight/lasers** through a **lens/prism**,

Herschel discovered **ultraviolet/infrared** radiation. His experiment was designed to measure

the **temperature/wavelength** of the different colours of light. He noticed that his measurements

increased/decreased from violet to red. He took a measurement just beyond the red end of the

visible light spectrum and found that it was even **colder/hotter** than the red light.

Q6   Ritter discovered a type of invisible radiation using similar apparatus to that shown below.

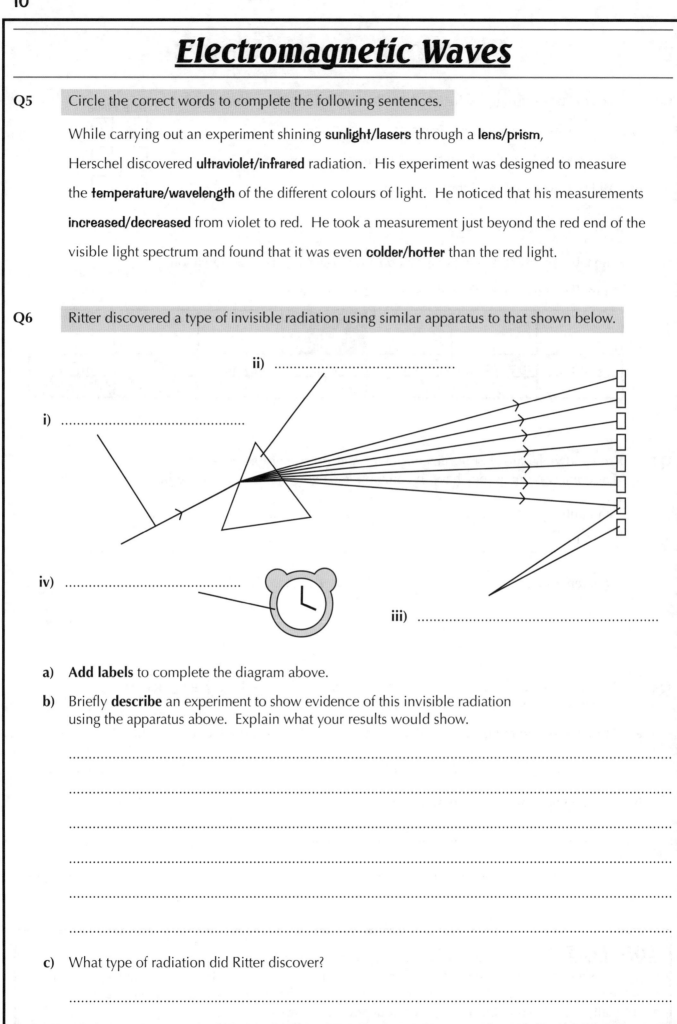

ii) ....

i) ....

iv) ....

iii) ....

a)   **Add labels** to complete the diagram above.

b)   Briefly **describe** an experiment to show evidence of this invisible radiation
using the apparatus above. Explain what your results would show.

....

....

....

....

....

c)   What type of radiation did Ritter discover?

....

The Dangers of Electromagnetic Radiation

Q1 Here are four different types of **electromagnetic wave**:

| visible light | microwaves | gamma rays | infrared |

a) Which has the **lowest frequency**? ....

b) Which carries the **most energy**? ....

c) Which can cause damage by **ionisation**? ....

d) Which has the **highest frequency**? ....

Q2 Sunlight contains **ultraviolet radiation**.
Explain why excessive sunbathing can be **dangerous**.

....

....

....

Q3 EM waves with **higher frequencies** are generally more **damaging**.

a) Explain, in terms of frequency, why some **ultraviolet** radiation
can be almost as damaging as **X-rays**.

....

....

b) Give two effects that EM waves can have when they are **absorbed by living cells**.

1. ....

2. ....

Q4 Mobile phones use **microwaves**.

a) Why might people be worried that a lot of mobile phone use might be harmful?

....

....

b) Explain why it isn't safe to use infrared radiation for mobile phones.

....

....

Radio Waves and Microwaves

Q1 The house shown below receives **radio broadcasts** from a nearby transmitter, even though there is a mountain between the house and the transmitter.

radio transmitter

Use the words below to fill in the blanks in the passage.

ionosphere   direct current   short-wave   long-wave   alternating current   absorbs   reflects

The house can receive .... signals because they can bend

(diffract) around the mountain. It also receives .... signals

because they are reflected by the ....

Q2 Microwaves are used for **cooking** as well as for mobile phone **communications**.

Explain why your body does not get 'cooked' when you use a mobile phone.

....

....

....

Q3 Gabrielle in Britain and Carwyn in Canada are talking by mobile phone. The mobile phone signals are sent via a communications satellite.

NOT TO SCALE

Communications Satellite

Gabrielle's phone

Carwyn's phone

Atlantic Ocean

a) Suggest why the satellite needs to be high above the Earth.

....

....

b) Why are microwaves good to use for satellite communications?

....

c) Name another type of EM wave that can be used in satellite transmissions.

....

P1a Topic 2 — The Electromagnetic Spectrum

Infrared Radiation

Q1 Use the words in the box to **complete the paragraph** about **infrared** radiation.

| bright | dark | electrical | heat | hot | night-vision |

Infrared is another name for .... radiation. People give out infrared because

they are .... The police use .... equipment to let them

see people in the .... The equipment changes infrared into an

.... signal which then appears as a .... spot on a screen.

Q2 Information can be transmitted quickly through **optical fibres**.

a) Tick the boxes to show whether these statements are **true** or **false**.   **True False**

   i) Optical fibres carry electromagnetic radiation.   ☐ ☐

   ii) Optical fibres work because the EM wave is refracted along the fibre.   ☐ ☐

b) Which of the following types of EM radiation is used in optical fibres?
Circle one answer.

     Radio   Microwaves   Ultraviolet   Infrared

Q3 Infrared radiation has many uses.

a) Give two examples of appliances that use infrared radiation for each of the following purposes.

   i) Cooking:

   ....

   ii) Wireless communication between electrical devices:

   ....

   ....

   ....

b) Describe how infrared radiation is used in security systems.

   ....

   ....

Top Tips: The prefix 'infra' comes from Latin. It basically means 'below' — so infrared
radiation is just radiation with a frequency below that of red light. The opposite of 'infra' is 'ultra',
which means above or beyond — so ultraviolet radiation is just...   You get the idea...

Visible Light, UV and X-rays

Q1   Eyes and cameras both use visible light in a similar way.

a)   Briefly describe how we are able to see objects with our eyes.

....

....

....

b)   Briefly describe how a camera forms and records an image.

....

....

Q2   **Ultraviolet radiation** is useful in detecting bank note forgeries.

a)   What does a **fluorescent** material do when exposed to ultraviolet radiation?

....

....

b)   Explain how banks can detect forgeries using **fluorescent ink** on their banknotes.

....

....

....

c)   Explain why you might use fluorescent ink to mark your name on a valuable object, e.g. a laptop.

....

....

Q3   **Ultraviolet radiation** can also be used to make water safer.

Explain how this is done.

....

....

Visible Light, UV and X-rays

Q4 Explain why it is safe to use fluorescent lamps, even though harmful UV rays are produced inside them.

....

....

....

Q5 Choose from the words below to complete this passage.

lead	plastic	bones	transmitted	soft tissue	aluminium	absorbed

X-rays sent through a person's body can pass easily through .... but are

.... more by .... Screens and shields made of

.... are used to minimise unnecessary exposure to X-rays.

Q6 Indicate whether the following statements about X-rays are **true** or **false**.

True False

a) X-rays can be used to look inside objects. ☐ ☐

b) Medical X-ray photographs show "shadows of our bones". ☐ ☐

c) Flesh is more dense than bone so it lets X-rays through more easily. ☐ ☐

Q7 Describe two ways in which X-rays are used in airports.

1. ....

....

2. ....

....

Top Tips: Crikey, even more uses of electromagnetic radiation. The examiners are mad keen on you knowing all the different uses. So make sure you know all the examples on the last few pages. Some of them you might be really familiar with, but it's important to learn all the less famous ones too.

Gamma Rays and Ionising Radiation

Q1   Complete the following paragraphs on radiotherapy using the words provided.

| ill | centre | normal | kill | cells | focused | cancer | dose | radiotherapy |

High doses of gamma radiation will .... living .... Because of this, gamma radiation is used to treat .... Gamma rays are .... on the tumour using a wide beam. Damage to .... cells can make the patient feel very .... This damage is minimised by directing the radiation at the tumour and using the minimum .... possible.

Q2   Some rocks in the Earth's crust give out ionising radiation.

a)   Circle the correct word below to show whether this statement is **true** or **false**.

Ionising radiation is emitted all the time from radioactive sources.   **True / False**

b)   Name **three** types of ionising radiation.

....

c)   Explain what is meant by the term '**ionising radiation**'.

....

....

Q3   The diagram shows how radiation can be used to sterilise surgical instruments.

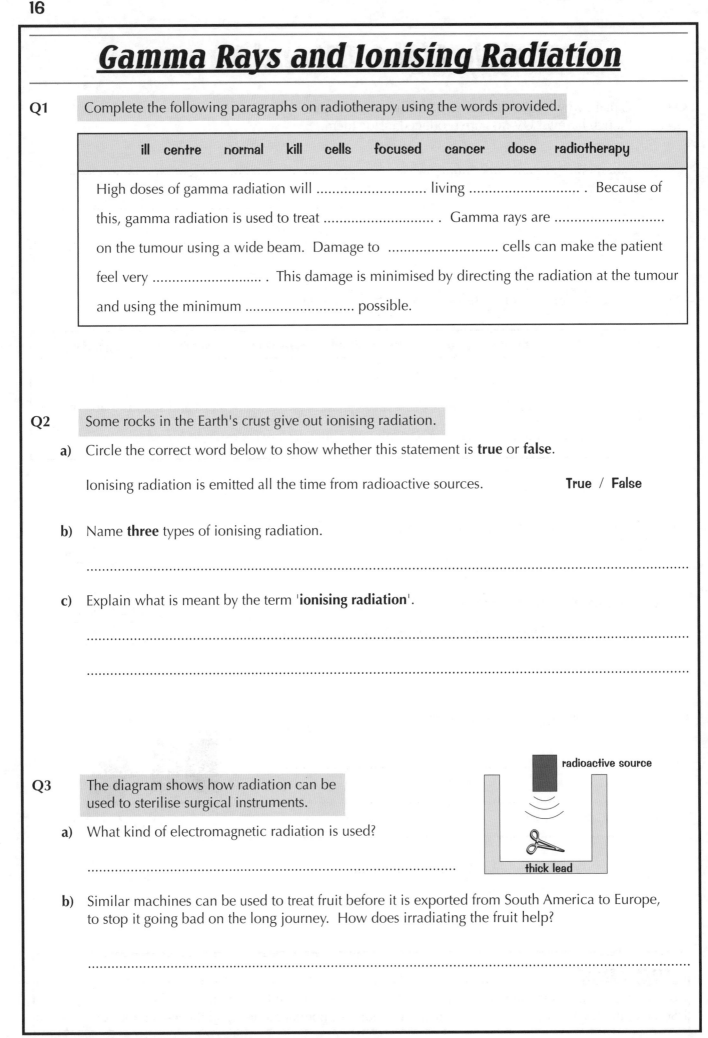

radioactive source

thick lead

a)   What kind of electromagnetic radiation is used?

....

b)   Similar machines can be used to treat fruit before it is exported from South America to Europe, to stop it going bad on the long journey. How does irradiating the fruit help?

....

The Solar System

Q1   Use the words in the box to **complete the paragraph**.

moons	Mercury	stars	Universe	Milky Way	Jupiter

The .... is made up of millions of galaxies. Our Solar System is in a galaxy

called the .... Each galaxy is made of billions of

.... Many planets have .... orbiting around them.

In our Solar System, the planets vary massively in size — .... is the smallest,

and .... is the biggest.

Q2   Even though the Earth's radius is a massive 6378 km,
it's very small compared to the scale of the Universe.

a)   Rearrange the following list of **astronomical things** into size order, starting with the smallest.

galaxy   moon   star   planet   Universe

.... ➡ .... ➡ .... ➡ .... ➡ ....

b)   Fill in the table of **astronomical distances** with the **numbers 1-4**, to put them into the
correct order of size. Make the smallest distance number 1 and the largest distance number 4.

	Distance between Earth and Sun
	Distance between stars
	Distance between galaxies
	Distance between Earth and Moon

Q3   Which one of the following statements is **not true**?
Tick the appropriate box.

☐   The planets in our Solar System vary in size.

☐   The Sun is the largest object in our Solar System.

☐   The Universe doesn't contain all of the galaxies.

☐   Our galaxy is larger than our Solar System.

Top Tips: The examiners really want you to be able to compare the relative sizes of the Earth,
the Moon, the planets, the Sun, galaxies and the Universe — and the distances between them too.
So if that last sentence wasn't a big enough hint — learn all that stuff and you'll be raking in the marks.

Is Anybody Out There?

Q1   Robot landers are sent to Mars to carry out **experiments**.

a)   Name one type of experiment that a lander might carry out.

   ....

b)   Explain **what** the experiments you named in **a)** are looking for.

   ....

   ....

c)   Give an **advantage** of remote sensing, compared to landing a robot on the surface of a planet.

   ....

   ....

Q2   The diagram shows a (made-up) **space probe** called **Erik** orbiting **Titan**, which is one of **Saturn's moons**.

not to scale

Erik

Titan

Saturn

Earth

a)   How would Erik **transmit data** back to Earth?

   ....

b)   Give **one** example of the type of data the probe might collect about the moon.

   ....

Q3 a)   What is the **aim** of the **SETI** project?

   ....

b)   What **evidence** do scientists on the SETI project look for?

   ....

   ....

c)   How can the **general public** help SETI with this?

   ....

Looking into Space

Q1 The graph below shows the amount different
electromagnetic waves are absorbed by the atmosphere.

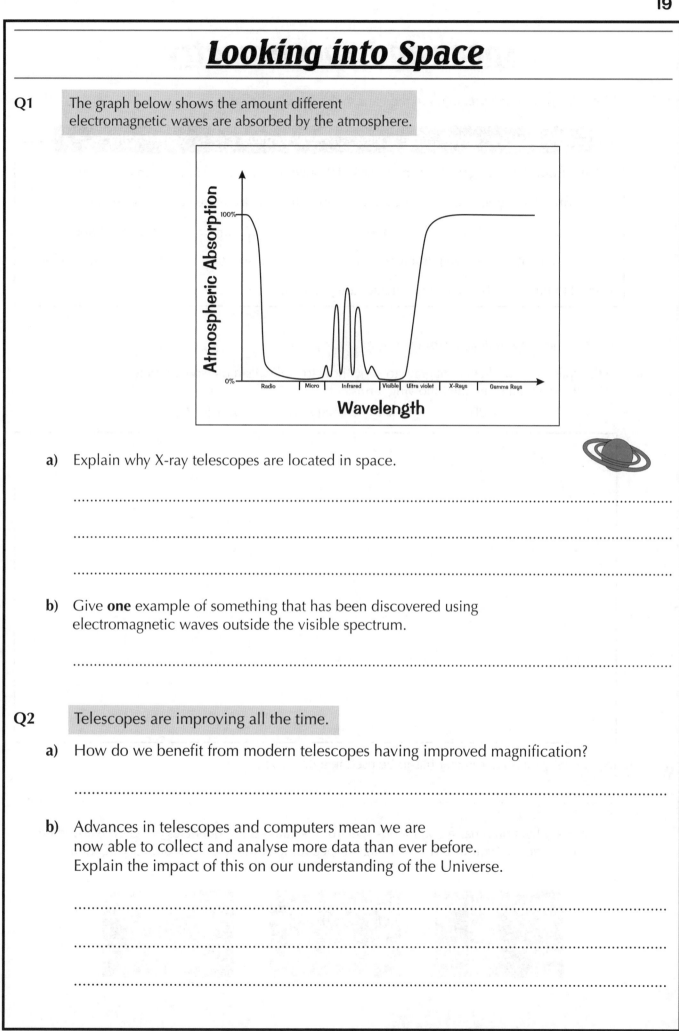

a) Explain why X-ray telescopes are located in space.

....

....

....

b) Give **one** example of something that has been discovered using
electromagnetic waves outside the visible spectrum.

....

Q2 Telescopes are improving all the time.

a) How do we benefit from modern telescopes having improved magnification?

....

b) Advances in telescopes and computers mean we are
now able to collect and analyse more data than ever before.
Explain the impact of this on our understanding of the Universe.

....

....

....

<u>*Space and Spectrometry*</u>

Q1   Use the words in the box to fill in the gaps in the passage below.

elements	dark	slit	absorption	wavelengths

Light from stars and galaxies can be passed though a .... in a spectrometer to form a spectrum. .... lines in the spectrum are caused by certain .... of light being absorbed by .... in the star's atmosphere. Each element has its own particular .... spectrum, so spectrometers can be used to find out what stars and galaxies are made of.

Q2   You can make a simple spectrometer from a box and a CD.

a) In the space below, draw a diagram to show how to make a simple spectrometer. Label the diagram using the following terms:

     CD   **light slit**   **eye slot**   **slot for CD**

b) Explain why the spectrometer has to be used in a dark room.

....

c) An ordinary light bulb has a continuous spectrum because no frequencies of light are absorbed. Circle the spectrum you would see through a spectrometer pointed at an ordinary light bulb.

The Life Cycle of Stars

Q1 A star in its **stable** phase **doesn't get bigger or smaller**, even though there are forces tending to make it expand and forces trying to make it contract.

a) What causes the outward pressure on the star?

....

b) What is the force pulling the star inwards? ....

c) Why doesn't the star expand or contract?

....

d) What is another name for a star in its stable phase? ....

Q2 Stars are formed from clouds of dust and gas called **nebulas**.

a) **Why** does the material come together?

....

b) Where does the **heat and light energy** emitted by a star come from?

....

Q3 Old stars eventually turn into **red giants**.

a) What causes a star to become a red giant? ....

....

b) Why is a red giant red? ....

....

Marilyn was nearing the end of her stable phase

Q4 Complete the passage below to describe what eventually happens to red giants.

A star with a similar mass to the Sun will eject gas and dust as a

...., leaving a dense core called a ....

A bigger star will explode as a ...., leaving a very dense core called

a .... The biggest stars will form a

.... instead.

Due to printing restrictions, red giants are currently unavailable.

The Origins of the Universe

Q1 **Complete this passage** using the words supplied below.

matter	energy	expand	explosion

Many scientists believe that the Universe started with all the ....

and .... in one small space.

There was a huge ...., and space and the material in it started

to ....

Q2 The '**Big Bang**' and '**Steady State**' theories are two theories of the origin of the Universe.

a) Briefly explain the idea behind the Steady State theory.

....

....

b) What does this theory suggest is happening as the Universe is expanding?

....

....

Q3 Francesca is standing by a busy street when an ambulance rushes past, sirens blaring.

a) As the ambulance moves away, how will the siren sound different to Francesca?
Underline the correct answer.

It will sound higher pitched   **It will sound lower pitched**

The higher the pitch, the higher the frequency.

b) Explain your answer to **a)** in terms of the change in frequency
and wavelength 'observed' by Francesca.

....

....

....

Q4 Which of the following statements is **not true**? Tick the appropriate box.

☐ Light from distant galaxies is at lower frequency than close ones.

☐ Galaxies further away from us have greater red-shifts than nearer ones.

☐ The light from distant galaxies has a lower wavelength than from those nearby.

The Origins of the Universe

Q5   Explain why the **red-shift** of galaxies provides evidence that the Universe is expanding.

....

....

....

Q6   The Big Bang theory and the Steady State theory are **two** models scientists use to explain the origin of the Universe.

a)   What is cosmic microwave background (CMB) radiation?

....

....

b)   Explain why the discovery of CMB radiation provided strong evidence for the Big Bang theory.

....

....

....

c)   What other evidence is there to support the Big Bang theory? Explain your answer.

....

....

d)   How does the Steady State theory explain the red-shift of galaxies?

....

....

e)   Do **most** scientists currently accept the Big Bang theory or the Steady State theory as the model for the origin of the Universe? Explain your answer.

....

....

Top Tips: There are loads of different ways of asking about the origins of the Universe. But they all rely on you knowing the basic facts and different pieces of evidence. So know which bits of evidence explain the two big theories — the Big Bang theory and the Steady State theory.

Mixed Questions — P1a Topics 1, 2 & 3

Q1 The waves A, B and C represent **infrared**, **visible light** and **ultraviolet** radiation (not in that order).

Tick the box next to any of the following statements which are **true**.

☐   B represents ultraviolet radiation.

☐   The infrared wave has the largest amplitude.

☐   C has the highest frequency.

☐   A has the shortest wavelength.

A

B

C

Q2 Infrared radiation is used by TV **remote controls**. Jake shows Peter that he can change the TV channel by pointing the remote control at a mirror on the opposite wall.

a) What property of EM rays has Jake demonstrated? Circle the correct answer.

       reflection   **refraction**   **diffraction**

b) Draw a ray on the diagram below to show the path of the radiation emitted from the remote control to the TV.

TV remote sensor

mirror

TV remote

Q3 A lander robot is sent to **look for signs of life** on Mars.

a) Describe one type of experiment that might be done by the lander.

....

b) The probe sends radio signals at a frequency of 95.6 MHz back to Earth. (Use $v = 3 \times 10^8$ m/s.)

Calculate the wavelength of the radio signals.

M stands for "Mega" and means "multiplied by 10^6".

....

....

Mixed Questions — P1a Topics 1, 2 & 3

Q4   The Sun consists mainly of **hydrogen**. It also contains **helium**.

a)   In a few million years time, the Sun will contain **more helium**
and **less hydrogen** than it does now. Explain why.

....

....

b)   The Sun is currently in its 'stable period'. What determines how long a star's stable period lasts?

....

....

c)   Will the Sun ever become a **black hole**? Explain your answer.

....

....

Q5   EM radiation can be extremely **useful**.

a)   Using the boxes below, number the following types of EM radiation in order of **decreasing**
frequency (1 = highest frequency). Write down one use for each type of radiation.

☐   Ultraviolet   ....

☐   X-rays   ....

☐   Infrared   ....

b)   SETI is an Earth-based project that searches for **narrow band radio waves** from space.

i) What does SETI stand for?

....

ii) Why are they only interested in narrow band waves rather than all radio waves?

....

....

c)   Explain how the **red-shift** of EM radiation produced by galaxies
can be used to show that the Universe is expanding.

....

....

....

Mixed Questions — P1a Topics 1, 2 & 3

Q6 Radio Roary transmits **long-wave** signals with a wavelength of **1.5 km**.

a) Calculate the **frequency** of Radio Roary's transmission. (Use speed = 3×10^8 m/s.)

....

....

b) Mr Potts is on holiday in the Scottish Highlands. The cottage he's staying in has a TV and radio. Mr Potts loves 'The Archers' on Radio 4, but finds that he can only get long-wave radio reception. TV reception is also very poor, so he can't watch his favourite cookery and gardening shows.

Explain why Mr Potts gets **good** long-wave radio reception, but such **poor** short-wave radio and TV reception.

....

....

c) Mr Potts' holiday cottage has a microwave oven. The microwaves used in ovens are different from those used to carry mobile phone signals. Explain how they differ, and why different types are used.

....

....

Q7 Cancer is sometimes treated using **gamma rays**.

a) Describe how gamma rays are used to treat cancer.

....

....

b) Give **one** other use of gamma rays.

....

c) Exposure to gamma rays can also cause cancer.
Describe the link between the frequency of EM radiation and how dangerous it is.

....

....

d) Gamma rays are one type of ionising radiation.
Name **two** other types and explain what 'ionising' means.

....

....

<u>Mixed Questions — P1a Topics 1, 2 & 3</u>

Q8   Our ideas about the structure of the Universe have **changed** over time.

a)   Describe the **differences** between the geocentric model and the heliocentric model.

....

....

b)   Explain the role **Galileo** played in providing evidence for the heliocentric model.

....

....

....   Galileo!

....

c)   Briefly describe the ways in which **modern** telescopes have helped
us **improve** our understanding of the Universe.

....

....

....

....

Q9   Simple telescopes use **converging lenses**.

a)   Some of the light rays entering a converging lens in a telescope **refract**.
Explain what is meant by refraction.

....

....

b)   Describe how a **reflecting** telescope works. Include the following words in your answer:

   large concave mirror   small concave mirror   focal point   hole   real image   eyepiece lens

....

....

....

....

....

P1b Topic 4 — Waves and the Earth

Ultrasound and Infrasound

Q1 Complete the following passage on foetal scanning using words from the list.

foetus	reflected	media	detected	echoes	body	image

Ultrasound waves can pass through most parts of the .... Whenever

an ultrasound wave reaches the boundary between two different ....,

some of the wave is .... back and can be .... These

.... can be processed by a computer to give an .... of

the ....

Q2 Indicate whether the following statements are **true** or **false**.

Ultrasound waves have frequencies greater than 20 000 Hz.

X-rays are safe to use for foetal scanning.

Some animals use ultrasound frequencies to communicate with one another.

Bats use ultrasound to sense their way around an environment.

True False
☐ ☐
☐ ☐
☐ ☐
☐ ☐

Q3 Number the following sentences 1 to 4 to describe how submarines use sonar to detect things in the water around them.

	These ultrasound waves reflect off objects like other boats, the sea bed and marine animals.
	The reflected waves are detected as they arrive back at the submarine.
	The submarine emits waves of ultrasound.
	Computers on board time the delay between emitting waves and detecting their reflections. They then use this to calculate how far away objects are.

Q4 A boat is using **ultrasound** to scan the seabed. There is a **1 s** delay between the ultrasound being emitted and detected.

a) If the speed of sound in the water is **1500 m/s**, how far away is the seabed?

Use speed = distance ÷ time

....

....

b) If the boat passes over a **wreck**, what will happen to the time taken to receive the echo?

....

Ultrasound and Infrasound

Q5 Some animals use **infrasound** to communicate.

a) What is meant by infrasound?

  ....

b) Explain **why** some animals use infrasound to communicate.

  ....

  ....

  ....

c) Describe two other uses of infrasound:

  1. ....

  ....

  2. ....

  ....

Q6 Ultrasound waves are used in foetal scanning.
The speed of ultrasound in soft tissue in the body is 1540 m/s.

During one scan, it takes 0.000045 s for a wave to travel from the scanner to the baby's head and back again. Calculate the distance of the baby's head from the scanner.

  ....

  ....

Q7 A pulse of ultrasound is used to find the size of a large crack under the ground, through which water is flowing.

Convert everything to SI units first ($\mu s = 1 \times 10^{-6}$ s).

The two reflected pulses are detected 130 μs apart.
If the speed of sound in the crack is 1400 m/s, calculate the width of the crack.

  ....

  ....

  ....

  ....

Top Tips: Ah, a spot of maths to dust away the cobwebs. These pages should have given you lots of practice in working out the distance of something using ultrasound. Know what ultrasound and infrasound are — and their uses. Then you'll be set to pick up some juicy marks in the exam.

The Earth's Structure

Q1 The Earth's outer layer is made up of tectonic plates. Describe what causes tectonic plates to move.

Blame it on the boogie.

....

....

....

Q2 Scientists find it difficult to predict earthquakes.

a) What causes earthquakes?

....

....

b) Describe one method that scientists can use to try to predict earthquakes.

....

c) Describe the problems with the method in part **b)**.

....

....

Q3 Paula carries out the experiment below to show the unpredictability of earthquakes.

a) What will eventually happen to the brick as Paula slowly adds masses to the mass holder?

....

....

....

....

Brick, Elastic cord, String, Pulley, Masses, Sandpaper, Bench

b) Suggest what might happen if Paula repeated the experiment in exactly the same way. You should discuss how this is similar to a real earthquake in your answer.

....

....

....

Seismic Waves

Q1   **Draw lines** to match each of these words with the **correct definition**. One has been done for you.

seismic waves

seismograph

P-waves

S-waves

longitudinal seismic waves

shock waves from an earthquake

a device that records seismic waves

seismic waves that cannot travel through liquids

Q2 a)   Tick the boxes to show whether the sentences are true or false.

True False

i) Seismic waves are caused by earthquakes and explosions.

ii) S-waves and P-waves can both travel through solids.

iii) All seismic waves are longitudinal waves.

iv) Seismic waves can be reflected but not refracted.

b)   Write out corrected versions of the **false** statements.

....

....

Q3   When there's an earthquake, **seismic waves** travel through the Earth.
S-waves and P-waves are two types of seismic wave.

a)   Why do both S and P waves **curve** as they travel through the Earth's mantle?

....

....

b)   Why do seismic waves abruptly change direction when they pass between the core and the mantle?

....

....

c)   Why are S-waves **not** detected at the Earth's surface immediately opposite the
site of the earthquake?

....

Top Tips: All the stuff on this page is fairly simple, but still really important. Make sure
you know what causes seismic waves. Learn about the two types of seismic waves too. Then reward
yourself with a pat on the head. Just the one though. We don't want you getting a big ego.

Seismic Waves

Q4 This **seismogram** shows the arrival of an
S-wave and a **P-wave** after an earthquake.

(diagram: traces labelled A and B along a time axis marked 0, 2, 4, 6 — **time after earthquake in minutes**)

a) Why do the two traces **not** arrive **together**?

....

b) Which trace shows the arrival of the P-wave — A or B?   ....

c) The average speed of the P-waves is **12 000 m/s** through the mantle.
Approximately how far was the seismometer from earthquake's epicentre?

wave speed = distance ÷ time

....

....

....

d) Describe two ways in which a seismogram recorded immediately opposite the site of the
earthquake's epicentre would be **different** from the one shown above.

1. ....

2. ....

Q5 Seismograms can be used to work out the distance
from a seismometer to an earthquake's epicentre.

a) Describe how three seismometers can be used to work out the exact location of
an earthquake's epicentre. You should include a sketch in your answer.

....

....

....

b) Explain why at least three seismometers are needed to
find the exact location of the earthquake's epicentre.

....

....

Electric Current and Power

Q1   Use the words below to fill in the gaps.

voltage   pressure   current   energy

> The rate of flow of charge around a circuit is called the ....
>
> .... is an electrical .... that pushes the current around
>
> the circuit. It gives a measure of the .... transferred.

Q2   Describe the **difference** between direct current (d.c.) and alternating current (a.c.).

....

....

Q3   The diagram shows three traces on the same **cathode ray oscilloscope** (CRO).
The settings are the **same** in each case.

A   **B**   **C**

Write down the **letter** of the trace that shows:

a) the highest peak voltage ....   **b)** direct current ....   **c)** the lowest a.c. voltage ....

Q4   **Fill in the gaps** using the **words below**. You might need to
use some of the words more than once, or not at all.

power   watts   current   what   how long   energy   voltage

Power is the .... transferred per second and is measured in ....

The total energy transferred by an appliance depends on .... it's used for and

its .... rating. The power of an appliance can be calculated using the formula:

power = ... × ....

Top Tips: Phew, lots of definitions on that page. To recap, know what current, voltage and
power all are. Be able to explain the difference between direct and alternating current too. And don't
go calling them d.c. current and a.c. current. Because that'd be direct current current etc. Chaos.

Electric Current and Power

Q5 Two filament lamps are plugged into a mains supply of **230 V**. **Lamp A** draws a current of **0.43 A** and **Lamp B** draws a current of **0.17 A**.

You'll need the equation which connects power, current and voltage for this question and the one below.

a) What is the power of:

i) Lamp A?

....

ii) Lamp B?

....

b) Which lamp is likely to be brighter? ....

Q6 The **current** an appliance draws depends on its **power** rating. Complete the table below, showing the power rating and current drawn by various appliances at mains voltage — **230 V**.

Appliance	Power (W)	Current (A)
Kettle	2600	
Radio	13	
Laptop computer		3.2
Lamp		0.17

CGP hide and seek tip #32

Q7 A simple experiment can be carried out to investigate the power consumption of a low-voltage **component** e.g. a lamp.

a) List all the equipment you would need.

....

....

b) Briefly describe how you would carry out the experiment, and how you would then use the data collected to calculate the power of the component.

....

....

....

....

....

Generating Electricity

Q1 Use the words in the box to **fill in the blanks** in these two paragraphs about generating electricity.

> moving   electromagnetic   magnet   coil   induction
> alternating   voltage   reverses   magnetic   complete

You can create a .... across an electrical conductor by .... a

magnet near the conductor. This is called ....

In generators, this is usually achieved by rotating a .... near a

.... of wire. The generator produces an .... current when it is

connected up to a .... circuit. The current alternates since the direction of the

.... field .... every time the magnet rotates by half a turn.

Q2 The diagram on the right shows the trace produced when a **coil** is connected to a cathode ray oscilloscope and a **magnet** is **rotated nearby**.

a) On the diagram, draw what the trace would look like if the magnet was rotated **faster**.

The amplitude and the frequency would change.

b) Apart from rotating the magnet faster, what **three other things** could you do to make the maximum current **larger**?

1. ....
2. ....
3. ....

Q3 The lights on Sebastian's bicycle are powered by a **dynamo**. Explain why the bicycle lights dim as he slows down.

....
....
....

Top Tips: You can tell why people thought electricity was magic in the olden days — wave a magnet near some wire and hey presto... you get some electricity. Make sure you know what to change to make the voltage generated change and you'll generate lots of marks.

P1b Topic 5 — Generation & Transmission of Electricity

Generating Electricity

Q4 Decide whether the following a.c. generators would produce a **larger**, a **smaller** or **the same** current as the generator in the box. Circle the correct answer.

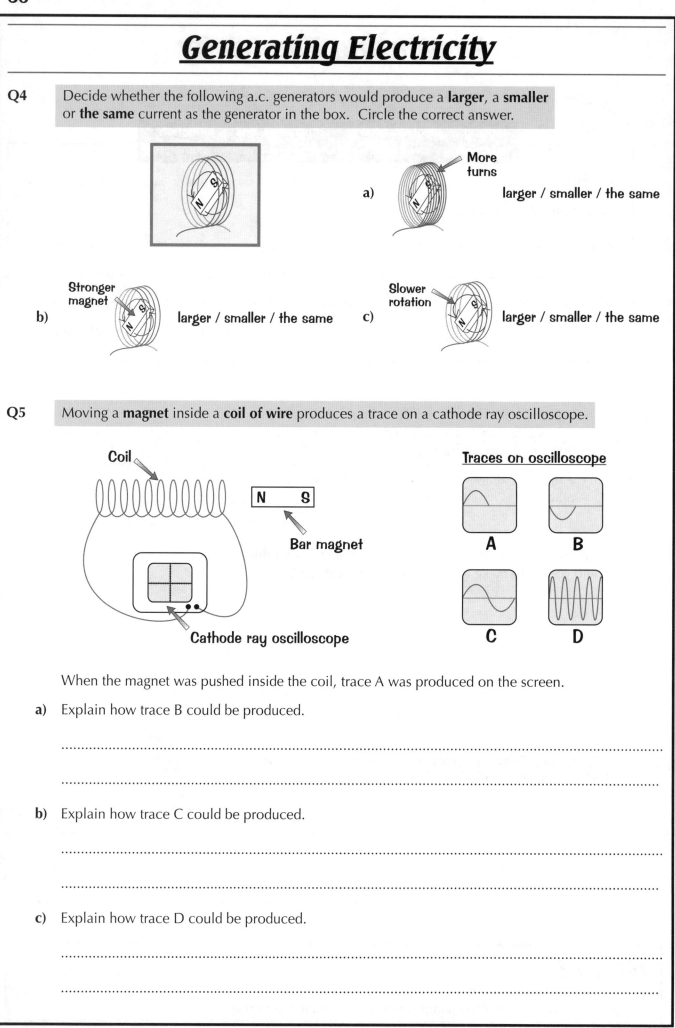

a) larger / smaller / the same

b) larger / smaller / the same

c) larger / smaller / the same

Q5 Moving a **magnet** inside a **coil of wire** produces a trace on a cathode ray oscilloscope.

When the magnet was pushed inside the coil, trace A was produced on the screen.

a) Explain how trace B could be produced.

....

....

b) Explain how trace C could be produced.

....

....

c) Explain how trace D could be produced.

....

....

Non-Renewable Energy and Power Stations

Q1 The three fossil fuels, coal, oil and gas, are 'non-renewable' energy sources.

a) Explain what 'non-renewable' means, in terms of energy resources.

....

....

b) How do the start-up times for fossil fuel power stations compare with nuclear power station start-up times?

....

Q2 Nuclear power is another example of a non-renewable energy resource.

a) Give **one** advantage of nuclear power.

....

b) Why is nuclear power so expensive?

....

....

Q3 Match up each environmental problem below with something that causes it.

Acid rain

Climate change

Dangerous radioactive waste

Spoiling of natural landscapes

Releasing CO_2 by burning fossil fuels

Coal mining

Sulfur dioxide formed by burning oil and coal

Using nuclear power

Q4 Lisa says: "Using nuclear power to make electricity is too dangerous."
Ben says: "Using fossil fuels is even more dangerous in the long run."

Who do you think is right? Explain your answer.

....

....

....

Using Renewable Energy Resources (1)

Q1 Explain what 'renewable' means, in terms of energy resources.

....

....

Q2 Tick the boxes to show whether each statement applies to **hydroelectric** power or **tidal** power or **both**.

Hydro Tidal

a) Is usually used in estuaries. ☐ ☐

b) Is a reliable way to generate electricity. ☐ ☐

c) It can provide an immediate response to increased electricity demand. ☐ ☐

d) It is used to generate electricity by spinning a turbine. ☐ ☐

Q3 **Tidal barrages** can be used to generate electricity.

What happens to make turbines go round?

a) Explain how a tidal barrage works.

....

....

....

b) Give one reason why tidal barrages aren't used in very many places.

....

....

Q4 Describe two possible problems with using **wave power** to generate electricity.

1. ....

....

2. ....

....

Top Tips: The advantage of revision is that you've got a good excuse to eat lots of biscuits. The disadvantage is that you have to revise for an exam. Boo. Talking of advantages and disadvantages — learn all the ones for hydroelectricity, wave power and tidal barrages. It's bound to be on the exam.

<u>Using Renewable Energy Resources (2)</u>

Q1   People often object to wind turbines being put up near to where they live.

   a)   List two reasons why they might object.

   1)..

   2)..

   b)   List two arguments in favour of using wind turbines to generate electricity.

   1)..

   2)..

Q2   Explain the advantages and disadvantages of using **solar cells** to generate electricity.

   ....

   ....

   ....

Q3   Tick the correct boxes to show whether these statements apply to generating electricity from **geothermal** energy, **biomass** or **both**.

	Biomass	Geothermal
a) Set-up costs are high.	☐	☐
b) Does not release CO_2.	☐	☐
c) Possible in any country in the world.	☐	☐
d) Reduces the need for landfill sites.	☐	☐

Q4   Explain why burning biomass is almost '**carbon neutral**'.

   ....

   ....

   ....

   ....

<u>Comparison of Energy Resources</u>

Q1   The city of Fakeville decides to replace
its old coal-fired power station.
They have to choose between using
gas, nuclear, wind or biomass.

Give one **disadvantage** of each choice:

a)   **Gas** ....

....

....

b)   **Nuclear** ....

....

c)   **Biomass** ....

....

Q2   Read the statement below.

"Tidal power is a **plentiful** and **reliable** source of energy."

Do you agree with the statement? Explain your answer.

I **agree** / **disagree** because ....

....

....

....

Q3   Give two possible arguments **in favour** of nuclear power.

1. ....

....

2. ....

....

Comparison of Energy Resources

Q4 At a public meeting, people are sharing their views about hydroelectric power.

We should use hydroelectric power more — it doesn't cause any pollution.

And it gives us loads of free energy.

But it makes a terrible mess of the countryside.

At least it's reliable — it always gives us electricity when we need it.

Brian　　　**Hillary**　　　**Sue**　　　**Liz**

Say whether you agree or disagree with each person's view, and explain your reasons.

a) I **agree** / **disagree** with Brian because ....

....

b) I **agree** / **disagree** with Hillary because ....

....

c) I **agree** / **disagree** with Sue because ....

....

d) I **agree** / **disagree** with Liz because ....

....

e) Outline two **advantages** of hydroelectric power which were not mentioned at the public meeting.

1)..

2)..

f) Outline two **disadvantages** of hydroelectric power not mentioned at the meeting.

1)..

2)..

Top Tips: These pages should have given you a nice summary of all the different advantages and disadvantages of large-scale electricity production. Remember, both non-renewable and renewable energy sources have their good bits and bad bits. Just make sure you know them. And job's a good 'un.

Electricity and the National Grid

Q1 Number these statements 1 to 5 to show the order of the steps that are needed to deliver energy to Mrs Miggins' house so that she can boil the kettle.

	An electrical current flows through power cables across the country.
	Mrs Miggins boils the kettle for tea.
	Electrical energy is generated in power stations.
	The voltage of the supply is raised.
	The voltage of the supply is reduced.

Q2 Using **high voltages** in power cables means you need some **expensive** equipment.

a) Explain why it is still **cheaper** to use **high voltages** for transmission.

....

....

b) What equipment is used to increase the voltage of the electricity for transmission?

....

c) What is used to reduce the voltage of the electricity before it arrives at the consumers homes? Explain why it is used.

....

....

Q3 Give two reasons why people might have concerns about living near power lines.

1. ....

....

2. ....

....

Q4 The **primary** coil of a transformer has **25** turns. The **secondary** coil has **50** turns. Calculate the primary voltage, if the secondary voltage is **30 V**.

Drum roll please for the turns ratio equation...

$$\frac{\text{primary voltage}}{\text{secondary voltage}} = \frac{\text{number of turns on primary}}{\text{number of turns on secondary}}$$

....

....

....

P1b Topic 5 — Generation & Transmission of Electricity

Electricity and the National Grid

Q5 Each of the following sentences is incorrect.
Write a correct version of each.

a) The National Grid transmits energy at **high voltage** and **high current**.

....

b) A step-up transformer is used to **reduce the voltage** of the supply before electricity is transmitted.

....

....

c) Using a **high current** makes sure there is not much energy **wasted**.

....

Q6 A transformer is used to **decrease** a voltage from 400 000 V to 240 V.

a) What type of transformer is this? Explain your answer.

....

....

b) If the primary coil has 20 000 turns, how many turns does the secondary coil have?

....

....

....

....

c) The number of coils on the secondary coil is reduced to 10. If the primary voltage and the number of primary coils both stay the same, calculate the new secondary voltage.

....

....

....

Top Tips: Ooh, that turns ratio equation is very versatile. You can rearrange it in lots of different ways. Make sure you know how to use it to work out missing voltages and the missing number of turns on a transformer, as well as where and why transformers are used. Maybe make a brew first...

Energy Efficiency & Cost-Efficiency

Q1   Match up the quantities used for calculating electricity costs with the correct units.

The **power** of an electrical appliance.

The **time** an appliance is used for.

The **price** of electrical energy.

The **electrical energy** used by an appliance.

pence per kilowatt-hour

kilowatt-hour (kWh)

hour (h)

kilowatt (kW)

Q2   All the units in the list below are units of **energy**, except for one.

kilowatt   kilowatt-hour   kWh   J

a)   Circle the 'odd one out'.

b)   What **is** this a unit of? ....

Q3   The amount of energy an appliance uses depends on its **power** and the **time** it's used for.

a)   Calculate how many **kilowatt-hours** of electrical energy a **2 kW** electric heater uses in 3 hours.

Energy used (kWh)   =   power (kW)   ×   time taken (hours)

=   .... ×   ....

=   .... kWh

b)   Boris gets his electricity supply from Ivasparkco. They charge 7 pence per kilowatt-hour.
Work out the cost of the energy calculated in part **a)**.

Cost of energy =   price of one kWh   ×   number of kWh

=   ....   ×   ....

=   .... pence

Top Tips: Make sure you use the right formulas for energy and cost. Remember to use the correct units for the cost formula — it's worked out using kilowatts, hours and kilowatt-hours. Simples.

Energy Efficiency & Cost-Efficiency

Q4 Mr Tarantino wants to buy **double glazing** for his house, but the salesman tries to sell him insulated window shutters instead. He says they are cheaper and more **cost-efficient**.

	Double glazing	Insulated window shutters
Initial Cost	£3000	£1200
Annual Saving	£60	£20
Payback time	50 years	

a) Calculate the **payback time** for insulated shutters and write it in the table.

b) Is the salesman's advice correct? Give reasons for your answer.

....

....

Q5 Two **washing machines** are on sale with the following labels.

Techno *A-rated*
Power: 2 kW
Average time of cycle: 30 mins
Price: £420

Sudso 2000 *Under £400*
Power: 2 kW
Average time of cycle: 45 mins
Price: £380

a) i) What is the energy consumption (in kWh) for each cycle for **Techno**?

....

ii) What is the energy consumption (in kWh) for each cycle for **Sudso**?

....

b) The Adejonwo family does **four cycles** of washing each **week**.

i) How much **energy** would they save in **one year** by using Techno instead of Sudso? Give your answer in kilowatt-hours (kWh).

....

ii) 1 kilowatt-hour costs 8p. How much **money** would the family save in one year by using the more expensive machine?

....

iii) What is the **payback time** for buying the more expensive machine?

....

iv) If the Adejonwo family's washing machine lasts 6 years, would it have been **cost-efficient** to buy the Techno? Explain your answer.

....

....

Energy Transfer

Q1 Use the words below to fill in the gaps.

converted   created   conservation

The Principle for the .... of Energy says:

Energy can never be .... or destroyed — it's only ever

.... from one form to another.

Q2 Complete the following **energy transfer diagrams** to show the **main** types of energy involved in:

a) a gas cooker, ... → heat energy ....

b) an electric buzzer, electrical energy .... → ....

c) a television screen, ... → ....

d) a wind-up toy car, ... → kinetic energy ....

e) a nuclear reactor. nuclear energy .... → ....

Q3 The diagram shows a **steam locomotive**.

Oil lamp   Coal

a) What form(s) of energy are there in the:

i) coal? ....

ii) hot steam (which powers the engine)? ....

b) Describe two **energy transfers** which take place on the locomotive.

1...

2...

Q4

Bruce is practising weightlifting.

a) When Bruce holds the bar still above his head, what kind of energy does the weight have?

....

b) Bruce had porridge for breakfast. Describe how the chemical energy in his porridge is transferred to the gravitational potential energy of the lifted bar.

....

....

c) When Bruce lets go of the weight, what happens to its energy?

....

Energy Transformations

Q1 Tick the boxes to show whether these statements are **true** or **false**.

True False

a) **Efficiency** is the proportion of energy transferred to **useful** forms. ☐ ☐

b) The **wasted energy** from a device is the energy it delivers that's not useful. ☐ ☐

c) The more **efficient** a device is, the more energy it **wastes**. ☐ ☐

d) The **useful energy** transferred by a device is never more than the **total energy** supplied to it. ☐ ☐

Q2 Here is an **energy flow diagram** for an electric lamp. Complete the sentences below.

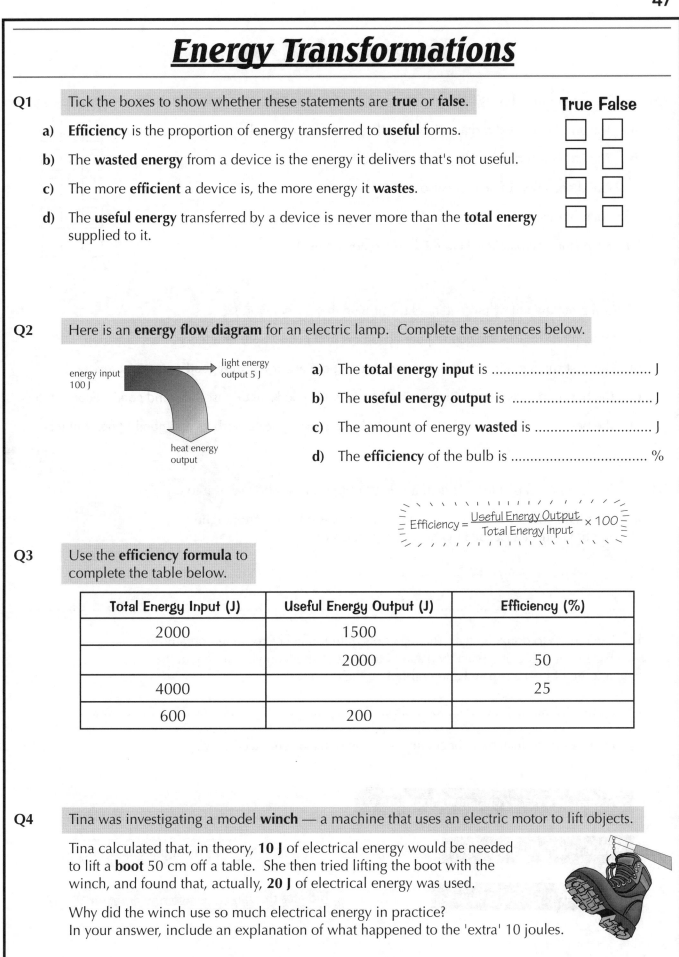

energy input 100 J

light energy output 5 J

heat energy output

a) The **total energy input** is .... J

b) The **useful energy output** is .... J

c) The amount of energy **wasted** is .... J

d) The **efficiency** of the bulb is .... %

$$Efficiency = \frac{Useful\ Energy\ Output}{Total\ Energy\ Input} \times 100$$

Q3 Use the **efficiency formula** to complete the table below.

Total Energy Input (J)	Useful Energy Output (J)	Efficiency (%)
2000	1500	
	2000	50
4000		25
600	200	

Q4 Tina was investigating a model **winch** — a machine that uses an electric motor to lift objects.

Tina calculated that, in theory, **10 J** of electrical energy would be needed to lift a **boot** 50 cm off a table. She then tried lifting the boot with the winch, and found that, actually, **20 J** of electrical energy was used.

Why did the winch use so much electrical energy in practice?
In your answer, include an explanation of what happened to the 'extra' 10 joules.

....

....

Heat Radiation

Q1 Tick the correct boxes below to show whether the sentences are true or false.

True False

a) The amount of heat radiation absorbed by a surface depends only on its colour. ☐ ☐

b) The hotter a surface is, the more heat it radiates. ☐ ☐

c) Good absorbers of heat are also good emitters of heat. ☐ ☐

d) Solar hot water panels use black pipes to reflect the heat. ☐ ☐

e) Silver survival blankets help the body to absorb heat. ☐ ☐

Q2 Complete the following sentences by circling the correct words.

a) Dark, matt surfaces are **good** / **poor** absorbers and **good** / **poor** emitters of heat radiation.

b) The best surfaces for radiating heat are **good** / **poor** absorbers and **good** / **poor** emitters.

c) The best materials for making survival blankets are **good** / **poor** absorbers and **good** / **poor** emitters.

d) The best surfaces for solar hot water panels are **good** / **poor** absorbers and **good** / **poor** emitters.

Q3 Sue makes a cup of tea. At first, it is too hot to drink so she leaves it to cool.

a) What can you say about the amount of heat **emitted** compared to the amount of heat **absorbed** by the tea, as it cools down?

....

....

b) Sue forgets to drink the tea. The tea cools until it reaches room temperature. The temperature of the tea then stays **constant**. What can you say about the amount of heat **absorbed** and **emitted** by the tea now?

....

c) Draw a line to match the beginning and end of each sentence below.

A system that's at a constant temperature...   ...radiates more power than it absorbs.

A system that's warming up...   ...radiates less power than it absorbs.

A system that's cooling down...   ...radiates the same average power that it absorbs.

Top Tips: Blimey, lots of definitions to learn. But it's really important you know them all. Now then, after all that I think we deserve a cup of tea. I'm parched, as my nana would say.

Heat Radiation

Q4 Tim did an experiment using a **Leslie's cube** to investigate the amount of heat different surfaces radiate.

Each surface on the cube had a different combination of **colour** and **texture**.

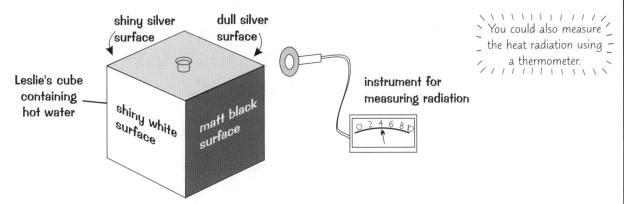

Tim measured the heat radiation coming from each surface. His results are shown below.

Surface	Reading	Colour and Texture
A	10	
B	4	dull silver
C	4	
D	2	

a) Complete the table to show which was:

i) the **matt black** surface,

ii) the **shiny silver** surface,

iii) the **shiny white** surface.

b) Use Tim's results to write a conclusion for his experiment.

....

....

....

c) Which of the surfaces A to D would be best to use for the outside of a refrigerator? Explain your answer.

....

....

Mixed Questions — P1b Topics 4, 5 & 6

Q1   A group of farmers live on a remote island, growing potatoes and farming llamas. They decide to put **solar cells** on the roofs.

a)   Suggest why the farmers have chosen to use solar power.

....

....

b)   Describe the main energy transfer in a solar cell.

....

c)   What other renewable sources of energy could the farmers use?

....

....

Q2   Dr Fergals has developed a new type of material, X, for **insulating** hot water tanks.

a)   Dr Fergals tests the new material and compares it with fibreglass wool. Complete the table below.

Type of lagging	Saving per year (£)	Initial cost (£)	Payback time (years)
Fibreglass wool	14.56	60	
Material X	29.12	100	

b)   Which material is the more cost-efficient? Explain your answer.

....

....

c)   Make suggestions about the nature of the surface of the material X. Explain your answer.

....

....

Q3   Earthquakes cause **seismic waves** to travel through the Earth.

a)   Say whether the following seismic waves are **transverse** or **longitudinal**:

P-waves: ....

S-waves: ....

b)   Both types of wave curve as they travel through the Earth.

Write down the name for this wave behaviour. ....

Mixed Questions — P1b Topics 4, 5 & 6

Q4　In one gas-fired power station, for every **1000 J** of energy input to the power station, 100 J is wasted in the **boiler**, 500 J is wasted in the **cooling water** and 50 J is wasted in the **generator**.

a)　What **type** of energy is contained in the **gas**? ....

b)　Calculate the **efficiency** of the power station.

....

....

c)　Electricity generated in power stations reaches our homes by a network of power cables.

i)　Explain why these power cables are at very high voltages.

....

....

ii)　Explain why the very high voltages are not dangerous for people **using** the electricity.

....

....

Q5　There are some frequencies of sound that humans **can't** hear.

a)　Write down the frequency range for each of the following types of sound waves.

Ultrasound: ....

Infrasound: ....

b)　Ultrasound can be used to calculate distances.

A pulse of ultrasound sent by a boat takes 3.2 seconds to travel from the boat to the sea bed and back again. If the speed of sound in sea water is 1520 m/s, how far away is the boat from the sea bed?

....

....

Use speed = distance / time

....

....

c)　Give **one** other use of ultrasound.

....

Mixed Questions — P1b Topics 4, 5 & 6

Q6 A lamp is being tested in a circuit.

a) The voltage across the lamp is 6 V and the current is 0.5 A.
Calculate the power of the lamp.

....

b) Another lamp has a power of 40 W. Calculate how much it would cost to use this
lamp for 4 hours every day, for a week. The cost of electricity is 13p per kWh.

....

....

Q7 The diagram shows a **generator** that is turned by a wind turbine.

a) What happens in the coil of wire when the magnet is rotated
at a constant speed? Explain your answer.

....

....

turned by wind
turbine

magnet

N S

soft iron

coil

b) The generator is attached to a cathode ray oscilloscope (CRO).

i) Circle the letter of the diagram that could show the output of the generator.

ii) Add labels to A and B to say which trace shows alternating current and which shows direct
current.

A

B

....

....

iii) Explain the difference between direct and alternating current.

....

....

c) Give one advantage and one disadvantage of using wind power to source all the UK's electricity.

....

....

Static Electricity

Q1 Fill in the gaps in these sentences with the words below.

electrons	positive	static	friction	insulating	negative

.... electricity can build up when two ....

materials are rubbed together. The .... moves ....

from one material onto the other. This leaves a .... charge

on one of the materials and a .... charge on the other.

Q2 **Circle** the pairs of charges that would attract each other and **underline** those that would repel.

positive and positive   positive and negative   negative and positive   negative and negative

Q3 The sentences below are wrong. Write out a **correct** version for each.

a) A polythene rod becomes negatively charged when rubbed with a duster because it loses electrons.

....

....

b) The closer two charged objects are together, the less strongly they attract or repel.

....

....

c) A material that loses electrons is left with a positive charge that is twice the lost negative charge.

....

....

Q4 What are the important similarities and differences between:

a) protons and neutrons?

....

....

b) protons and electrons?

....

....

Static Electricity

Q5 Match up these phrases to describe what happens in a **thunderstorm**.
Write out your complete sentences below in the correct order.

If the voltage gets big enough...

... the voltage gets higher and higher.

The bottoms of the clouds become negatively charged...

... and electrons are transferred between them.

As the charge increases...

... there is a huge spark (a flash of lightning).

Raindrops and ice bump together...

... because they gain extra electrons.

1. ....

2. ....

3. ....

4. ....

Q6 Three friends are talking about **static electricity**.

Why does my jumper crackle when I take it off?

Do cotton clothes get charged as much as nylon clothes?

How come I get zapped by my car door every time I get out?

Steph

Dan

Laura

Answer their questions in the spaces below.

Steph: ....

....

Laura: ....

....

Dan: ....

....

Static Electricity

Q7 Tick whether each of these statements is **true** or **false**.

	True	False
a) A charged comb can pick up small pieces of paper if they are placed near it.	☐	☐
b) A charged object can force electrons in an uncharged object to move — this is called induction.	☐	☐
c) Electrically charged objects can attract other objects — but only if they are charged too.	☐	☐

Q8 Jonny walks across a **nylon** carpet wearing **rubber-soled** trainers. When he goes to open the **metal** door handle he gets an electric shock. Explain why.

....

....

....

....

Q9 Wayne rubs a balloon against his nylon sweater.

a) Describe what happens to the **electrons** in the atoms on the surface of his sweater, and the effect this has on the **charge** of the balloon.

....

....

....

....

b) After rubbing the balloon on his sweater, Wayne holds it up against a wall and it sticks. Explain, in terms of charges, why the balloon sticks to the **uncharged** wall.

....

....

....

Top Tips: Static electricity is responsible for many of life's little annoyances — bad hair days, and those little shocks you get from touching car doors and even stroking the cat. Still, it can be kinda cool too — thunderstorms can be spectacular and hours of fun can be had with a balloon...

<u>*Uses and Dangers of Static Electricity*</u>

Q1 Choose from the words below to complete the passage.

fuel   explosion   tankers   wood   petrol   sparks   plastic   earthed

> Static electricity can be dangerous when refuelling aircraft. If too much static builds up, there
>
> might be .... which could set fire to the ....
>
> This could lead to an .... To prevent this happening, the nozzle of
>
> the filler pipe is .... so the charge is conducted away. There are similar
>
> safety problems with fuel .... and .... stations.

Q2 The sentences below are wrong. Write out a **correct** version for each.

a) Fuel tankers are earthed when refuelling using an insulating strap.

....

....

b) If a positively charged object is connected to earth by a metal strap, electrons flow
through the strap from the object to the ground, and the object is safely discharged.

....

....

Q3 The diagram shows an electrostatic paint sprayer.

a) How do the drops of paint become charged?

....

b) Why does this help produce a fine spray?

....

c) Explain how the paint drops are attracted to the object being sprayed.

....

....

d) Give **one** other use of electrostatic sprayers.

....

Charge and Current

Q1 Fill in the gaps in the paragraph with the words below. You may need some words more than once.

time	carried	rate	current	electrons	metals

Electric current is the .... of flow of charge — the amount of

charge that passes a point over a certain amount of ....

Charge has to be .... by something. In ....

the charge carriers are .... — negatively charged particles that are

free to move. Therefore, in these conducting materials, the ....

is simply the flow of ....

Q2 The diagram shows three traces on the same oscilloscope. The settings are the same in each case.

A   **B**   **C**

Write down the **letter(s)** of the trace(s) that show:

a) current from an a.c. supply. ....

b) current from a battery. ....

c) the highest d.c. voltage. ....

d) current that flows in only one direction. ....

Q3 The table below shows data from an experiment comparing three lamps, A, B and C.

	Lamp A	Lamp B	Lamp C
Time lamp is switched on (s)	2	4	
Current through lamp (A)	3		2
Charge transferred (C)		12	10

Calculate the **missing values** and write them in the table.

Q4 A 3 volt battery can supply a current of 5 amps for 20 minutes before it needs recharging. Calculate how much charge the battery can provide before it needs recharging.

....

....

....

Electric Current and Potential Difference

Q1 Use the words in the box to fill in the gaps. Use each word once only.

> more   voltage   resistance   less   current   force

a) The flow of electrons round a circuit is called the ....

b) .... is the .... that pushes the current round the circuit.

c) If you increase the voltage, ... current will flow.

d) If you increase the ...., ... current will flow.

Remember, voltage and potential difference both mean the same thing.

Q2 The following statements are wrong.
Write out a correct version of each.

a) In a circuit, the larger the potential difference, the less energy is transferred per unit of charge.

....

....

b) One ampere (amp) is the same as one coulomb per joule.

....

c) One volt is the same as one joule per ampere.

....

d) Voltage is conserved at circuit junctions.

....

Q3 The diagram opposite shows a **parallel** circuit. Ammeter
A_2 has a reading of **0.27 A** and A_3 has a reading of **0.43 A**.

a) What reading is shown on ammeter A_1?
Circle the correct answer.

   0.16 A   0.7 A   0.43 A

b) Explain your answer.

....

....

....

Resistance and V = I × R

Q1 Match up these items from a standard test circuit with the **correct description** and **symbol**.

ITEM	DESCRIPTION	SYMBOL
Cell	The item you're testing.	—(A)—
Variable Resistor	Provides the voltage.	—[⁄]—
Component	Used to alter the current.	—||—
Voltmeter	Measures the current.	—(V)—
Ammeter	Measures the voltage.	—[ ]—

Q2 Write down:

World's Strongest Current

a) the **unit** of:

i) current .... **ii)** voltage .... **iii)** resistance ....

b) two ways of **decreasing** the current in a standard test circuit:

1. ....

2. ....

Q3 Indicate whether these statements are **true** or **false**.
Write out a **correct version** of the false statements.

True False

a) The current in a circuit can be changed using a variable resistor. ☐ ☐

b) An ammeter should be connected in parallel with a component. ☐ ☐

c) Items that are in series can be in any order. ☐ ☐

d) A voltmeter should be connected in series with a component. ☐ ☐

....

....

....

....

Q4 On one particularly rock 'n' roll Saturday night, Jeremy decided to use a standard test circuit to find the resistance of a **fixed resistor**. He found a current of **0.2 A** flowed through the resistor when connected to a **3 V** power supply. Calculate the resistance of the resistor.

....

....

Resistance and V = I × R

Q5 Match the correct label to each of the **V-I graphs** below.

FIXED RESISTOR   FILAMENT LAMP   DIODE

A ....   B ....   C ....

Q6 Indicate whether the following are **true** or **false**.
Write out a **correct version** of the false statements.

		True	False
a)	The resistance of a filament lamp decreases as it gets hot.	☐	☐
b)	A current of 0.5 A will flow through a 2 Ω fixed resistor connected to a 3 V battery.	☐	☐
c)	Current can flow freely through a diode in both directions.	☐	☐
d)	The current through a fixed resistor at constant temperature is proportional to the voltage.	☐	☐
e)	Current can flow both ways through a filament lamp.	☐	☐

....

....

....

....

Q7 The graph below shows V-I curves for four resistors.

a) Calculate the resistance of resistor C.

....

b) Calculate the resistance of resistor B.

....

c) State which of the four resistors has the highest resistance.

....

You don't have to calculate the resistance of each resistor — think about how the gradient relates to resistance.

Devices and Resistance

Q1 Fill in the gaps using the words in the box.

power	current	how long	potential

The total energy transferred by an appliance depends on

.... it's used for and its ....

The power of an appliance can be calculated using the formula:

power = ... difference × ....

Q2 Tick the boxes to show whether the following statements are **true** or **false**.

	True	False

a) LDRs and thermistors are types of **variable** resistor.

b) An LDR has a **high** resistance in very **bright** light.

c) The resistance of a thermistor **increases** as the temperature **decreases**.

d) An LDR could be part of a useful thermostat.

Q3 Leyla was doing her homework when the **light** on her desk **went out**. Leyla's mum says the **bulb** has blown and needs replacing, but that they should wait till it **cools down** before touching it.

a) Explain what causes the filament in the lamp to get hot when current passes through it. Your answer should include the words **ions**, **electrons** and **lattice**.

....

....

....

b) Why are the filaments in lamps designed to have a very high resistance?

....

....

Top Tips: Wow... power, thermistors, LDRs, current, energy AND resistors — this page really is full to the brim with physics joy. Make sure you know all about power and energy transfer, as well as how electrons heat up a resistor as they travel through it.

Devices and Resistance

Q4   An electric heater is rated at **230 V**, **1500 W**.
Calculate the current it uses. Circle the correct answer below.

6.5 A   0.15 A   4.6 A   0.7 A

Q5   Lucy is comparing **three lamps**. She connects each lamp in a circuit
and measures the **current**. Her results are shown in the table below.

Complete the table by filling in the missing values.

	Lamp A	Lamp B	Lamp C
Voltage (V)	12	3	230
Current (A)	2.5	4	0.1
Power (W)			
Energy transferred in one minute (J)			

Q6   When a current flows through a resistor, some energy is transferred to
the resistor and causes it to **heat up**. Suggest **two** reasons why many
electrical devices are designed to **minimise** this heating effect.

1. ....

....

2. ....

....

Q7   Dale loves a bit of DIY, and is drilling holes to put up some shelves.
His electric drill is attached to a **12 V** battery and uses a current of **2.3 A**.

a)   Write down the equation that relates current, voltage, electrical energy transferred and time.

....

b)   If it takes Dale 30 seconds to drill one hole, how much energy
will be transferred by the motor if he drills **eight** holes?

....

....

Velocity and Acceleration

Q1 Which of the following are **vector quantities**? Circle the correct answers.

displacement   speed   velocity   acceleration   distance

Q2 A pulse of laser light takes 1.3 seconds to travel from the Moon to the Earth. The speed of light is approximately 3×10^8 m/s. How far away is the Moon from the Earth? Give your answer in km.

....

....

....

Q3 Ealing is about 12 km west of Marble Arch. It takes a tube train 20 minutes to get to Marble Arch from Ealing.

Only **one** of the following statements is true. Circle the appropriate letter.

A The average speed of the train is 60 m/s.

B The average velocity of the train is 10 m/s.

C The average velocity of the train is 60 m/s due east.

D The average speed of the train is 10 m/s.

E The average velocity of the train is 10 m/s due west.

Q4 An egg is dropped from the top of the Eiffel tower. It hits the ground after **8 seconds**, at a speed of **80 m/s**.

a) Calculate the egg's acceleration.

....

b) How long did it take for the egg to reach a velocity of 40 m/s?

....

Q5 A car accelerates at **2 m/s²**. After **4 seconds** it reaches a speed of **24 m/s**.

How fast was it going before it started to accelerate?

....

....

D-T and V-T Graphs

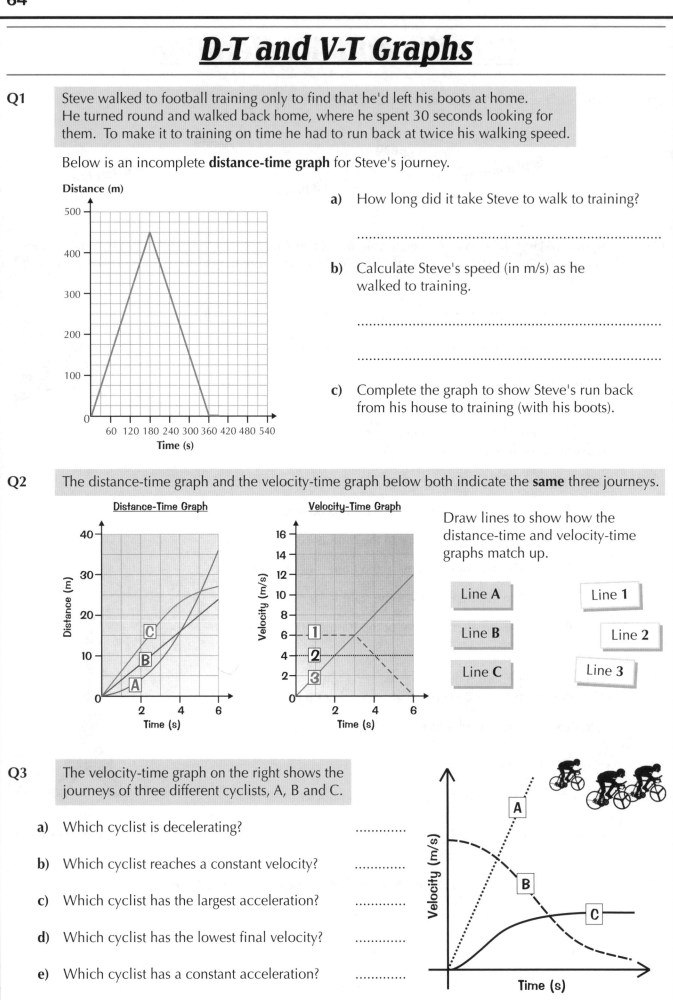

Q1 Steve walked to football training only to find that he'd left his boots at home. He turned round and walked back home, where he spent 30 seconds looking for them. To make it to training on time he had to run back at twice his walking speed.

Below is an incomplete **distance-time graph** for Steve's journey.

a) How long did it take Steve to walk to training?

....

b) Calculate Steve's speed (in m/s) as he walked to training.

....

....

c) Complete the graph to show Steve's run back from his house to training (with his boots).

Q2 The distance-time graph and the velocity-time graph below both indicate the **same** three journeys.

Draw lines to show how the distance-time and velocity-time graphs match up.

Line **A**   Line **1**

Line **B**   Line **2**

Line **C**   Line **3**

Q3 The velocity-time graph on the right shows the journeys of three different cyclists, A, B and C.

a) Which cyclist is decelerating? ....

b) Which cyclist reaches a constant velocity? ....

c) Which cyclist has the largest acceleration? ....

d) Which cyclist has the lowest final velocity? ....

e) Which cyclist has a constant acceleration? ....

D-T and V-T Graphs

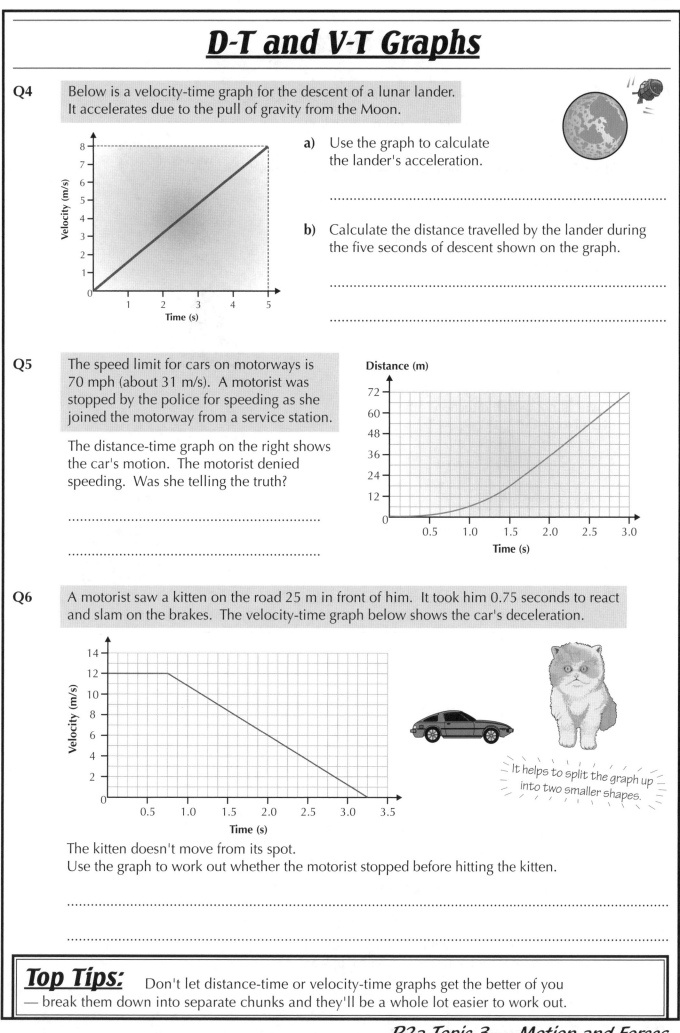

Q4   Below is a velocity-time graph for the descent of a lunar lander.
It accelerates due to the pull of gravity from the Moon.

a)   Use the graph to calculate
the lander's acceleration.

....

b)   Calculate the distance travelled by the lander during
the five seconds of descent shown on the graph.

....

....

Q5   The speed limit for cars on motorways is
70 mph (about 31 m/s). A motorist was
stopped by the police for speeding as she
joined the motorway from a service station.

The distance-time graph on the right shows
the car's motion. The motorist denied
speeding. Was she telling the truth?

....

....

Q6   A motorist saw a kitten on the road 25 m in front of him. It took him 0.75 seconds to react
and slam on the brakes. The velocity-time graph below shows the car's deceleration.

*It helps to split the graph up
into two smaller shapes.*

The kitten doesn't move from its spot.
Use the graph to work out whether the motorist stopped before hitting the kitten.

....

....

Top Tips: Don't let distance-time or velocity-time graphs get the better of you
— break them down into separate chunks and they'll be a whole lot easier to work out.

Forces

Q1 The forces acting on a balloon floating at a constant height are shown by the **force diagram** below.

The sentences below describe the balloon's motion.
Circle the correct word(s) in each sentence.

a) There is a greater driving force in the **east / west** direction.

b) The balloon will **rise / fall / stay at the same height**.

Q2 A bear rides a bike north at a constant speed.

a) Label the forces acting on the bear.

b) The bear brakes and slows down.
Are the forces balanced **as** he slows down? If not, which direction is the overall force in?

Q3 A teapot sits on a table.

a) Explain why it **doesn't** sink into the table.

b) Jane picks up the teapot and hangs it from the ceiling.
Label the forces acting on the teapot suspended by the rope on the picture below.

Show the direction of each force and make sure the size of each arrow relates to the size of the force.

c) The rope breaks and the teapot accelerates towards the floor.

i) Are the vertical forces balanced? Explain your answer.

ii) The teapot hits the floor without breaking and bounces upwards.
Which force causes the teapot to bounce upwards?

P2a Topic 3 — Motion and Forces

Weight and Terminal Velocity

Q1 Use the words supplied to fill in the blanks in the paragraph.

terminal	balances	increases	constant	greater	accelerates

An object is dropped from a height and falls through the atmosphere. At first, its weight is

.... than the air resistance acting on it, so it ....

downwards. As its speed increases, the air resistance .... until it

.... its weight. At this point, its velocity is .... — its

acceleration is zero and the object is said to have reached its .... velocity.

Q2 Two mad scientists are planning a trip to Mars.

a) Professor White tells Professor Brown —

"**We won't need so much fuel for the return trip — the rocket will have less mass on Mars.**"

Is Professor White's reasoning correct? Explain your answer.

....

....

b) Professor Brown wants to investigate gravity on Mars. He takes to Mars a small fire extinguisher which weighs 50 N on Earth. He also takes his Newton scales.

On Mars, Professor Brown weighs the fire extinguisher.
The scales read **19 N**.
Calculate the **gravitational field strength** on Mars.

Find the mass of the fire extinguisher first. Remember that on Earth, g = 10 N/kg.

....

....

Q3 A scientist plans to travel to the moon to perform an experiment. He will drop a **hammer** and a **feather** from the same height.

The scientist hypothesises that if he dropped both at the same time, the hammer would land before the feather. Is he correct? Explain your answer.

The moon's atmosphere is so thin you can treat it as a vacuum.

....

....

....

....

Forces and Motion

Q1 a) Tick the correct boxes to show whether the sentences are true or false.

True False

i) A resultant force is the overall force acting on a body. ☐ ☐

ii) An object will remain stationary if there is zero resultant force acting on it. ☐ ☐

iii) For an object to keep travelling at a steady speed, it must have an overall force acting on it. ☐ ☐

iv) If all the forces on an object are balanced, it is said to have a resultant force acting on it. ☐ ☐

b) Write a correct version of each false sentence in the space below. ☐ ☐

....

....

....

....

Q2 A **flamingo** is standing on one leg.

a) Two forces, A and B, are shown on the diagram to the right. Label the force marked B.

b) Complete the following sentences about the two forces:

Force A is exerted by the .... on the

.... Force B is exerted by the

.... on the ....

B ↑ ....

↓ A

c) Are force A and force B equal in size? Explain your answer.

....

....

Q3 Otto is driving the school bus at a **steady speed** along a level road. Tick the boxes next to any of the following statements which are **true**.

☐ The driving force of the engine is bigger than the friction and air resistance combined.

☐ The driving force of the engine is equal to the friction and air resistance combined.

☐ There are no forces acting on the bus.

☐ No force is required to keep the bus moving.

Forces and Motion

Q4 Complete the following passage.

When an object exerts a .... on another object, it experiences a force in return. For example, if Martin leans on a wall with a force of 150 N, the wall exerts a force of .... N in the opposite direction — an '................................. and ....' reaction. The force Martin exerts is called the .... force and the force the wall exerts is called the .... force.

Q5 Which of the following statements correctly explains what happens when you walk? Circle the appropriate letter.

A Your feet push the ground backwards, so the ground pushes you forwards.

B The force in your muscles overcomes the friction between your feet and the ground.

C The ground's reaction can't push you backwards because of friction.

D Your feet push forwards, and the ground's reaction is upwards.

Q6 Kate and William are having a bit of a skate. William gives Kate a push with a force 250 N.

a) Give the force of Kate on William.

....

b) Who will accelerate the most?
Explain your answer.

....
....
....
....
....

Kate
mass = 48 kg

mass = 83 kg
William

Top Tips: Remember that force is a vector quantity — it has a magnitude (an amount) and a direction. This is particularly important when drawing and interpreting force diagrams. Whenever one force acts, you get another one acting in the opposite direction. You can see this for yourself the next time you go swimming — when you push the water backwards, the water pushes you forwards.

Force and Acceleration

Q1 Use the words below to fill in the blanks. You won't have to use all the words.

mass	force	accelerates	opposite	resultant	inversely

If an object has a .... force acting on it, it ....

in the direction of the .... The acceleration depends on the size

of the force and on the .... of the object.

Q2 State whether the **forces** acting on these objects are **balanced** (zero resultant force) or **unbalanced**. Explain your answers.

a) A **cricket ball** slowing down as it rolls along the outfield.

....

b) A **vase** knocked off a window ledge.

....

c) A **bag of rubbish** which was ejected from a spacecraft in empty space.

....

Q3 The table below shows the **masses** and **maximum accelerations** of four different antique cars.

Write down the names of the four cars in order of increasing driving force.

1. ....

2. ....

3. ....

4. ....

Car	Mass (kg)	Maximum acceleration (m/s²)
Disraeli 9000	800	5
Palmerston 6i	1560	0.7
Heath TT	950	3
Asquith 380	790	2

Q4 Jo and Bob's scooters have the same engine. Bob and his scooter have a combined mass of 110 kg and an acceleration of 2.80 m/s². On her scooter, Jo only manages an acceleration of 1.71 m/s².

a) What **force** can the engine exert?

....

b) Calculate the combined mass of Jo and her scooter.

....

Force and Acceleration

Q5   Maisie drags a **1 kg** mass along a table with a newton meter so that it accelerates at **0.25 m/s²**. The newton meter reads **0.4 N**. Calculate the force of friction between the mass and the table.

....

....

Q6   A camper van of mass 2500 kg drives along a straight, level road at a constant speed.

a)   At this speed, air resistance is 2000 N and the friction between the wheel bearings is 500 N.

  i) What force is the engine exerting? ....

    ....

  ii) Draw a diagram to show
       all the horizontal forces
       acting on the camper van.
       Give the size of each force.

b)   A strong headwind begins blowing, with a force of **200 N**.
       The van slows down. Calculate its deceleration.

    ....

Q7   Jen and Sarah conduct an experiment to investigate the relationship between
       force and **acceleration**. They set up the experimental apparatus shown below.

a) Explain what the masses attached
       to the trolley are used for.

       ....

       ....

b) Describe how the **light gate** and **data logging software** are used in the investigation.

    ....

    ....

    ....

c) Describe the **relationship** between force and acceleration you would expect them to find.

    ....

    ....

Mixed Questions — P2a Topics 1, 2 & 3

Q1   Norman loves trainspotting. As a special treat, he not only notes
the train numbers but plots a **distance-time** graph for two of the trains.

a)   For how long is train 2 stationary?

....

b)   Both trains start at a steady speed.
How can you tell this from the graph?

....

c)   Calculate the initial speed of the faster train.

....

d)   Describe the motion of train 1 between 40 s and 80 s.

....

Q2   In the film 'Crouching Sparrow, Hidden Beaver',
a dummy is dropped from the top of a building.

a)   Sketch a distance-time graph and a velocity-time graph for the dummy
from the moment it is dropped until just after it hits the ground.
(Ignore air resistance and assume the dummy does not reach a terminal velocity.)

b)   Do any forces act on the dummy when it lies still on the ground (after falling)? If so, what are they?

....

c)   The take doesn't go to plan so the dummy is lifted back to the top of the building using a
760 W motor. If the motor uses the mains voltage (**230 V**), calculate the current through it.

....

d)   The film's director decides to use a taller building for the scene. Falling from this new building,
the dummy reaches its terminal velocity. Explain what is meant by 'terminal velocity'.

....

....

....

Mixed Questions — P2a Topics 1, 2 & 3

Q3 Scott water-skis over a 100 m course. When he reaches the end of the course, Scott lets go of the tow rope.

a) The graph below shows how Scott's velocity changed over the course. Describe his **acceleration**:

   i) between 0 and 5 seconds,

   ....

   ii) between 5 and 22 seconds,

   ....

   iii) after 30 seconds.

   ....

b) How far did Scott travel in the first 20 seconds?

....

....

c) A newton meter on the tow rope registers that Scott is being pulled with a force of 475 N. What was the **total combined force** of air resistance and friction between his water skis and the water between 10 and 25 seconds? Explain your answer.

....

....

Q4 Paul sets off from a junction on his scooter which produces a thrust of 270 N. The total mass of Paul and his scooter is 180 kg. For the following questions, assume air resistance is negligible.

a) Calculate the initial acceleration of Paul's scooter.

....

b) Calculate the size of the force produced when Paul applies his brakes and decelerates at **5 m/s²**.

....

c) Paul had reached a speed of **17.5 m/s** before he began to decelerate. Assuming he decelerates steadily, how many seconds will it take him to stop completely?

....

d) Paul picks up a large package and carries it on his scooter. Calculate the mass of the package if his initial acceleration when he sets off again is **1.45 m/s²**, but the thrust of the scooter remains **270 N**.

....

....

Mixed Questions — P2a Topics 1, 2 & 3

Q5 The diagram shows an aircraft being refuelled.
No safety precautions have been taken.

a) **i)** Explain how static electricity could cause an explosion in this situation.

....

....

ii) Give one precaution that can be taken to avoid this danger.

....

b) Write down one example of how static electricity is **useful**.

....

Q6 A temperature sensor containing a thermistor is used to monitor the temperature
of a room. The sensor is connected to a circuit containing a filament bulb.
As the temperature increases, the bulb's brightness increases.

a) What is a thermistor?

....

b) Explain why the filament in the bulb glows when a current flows through it.

....

....

....

c) The filament bulb is connected to a 25 V electricity supply.

i) Calculate the resistance of the filament bulb if it has a current of 4 A flowing through it.

....

ii) Calculate how much energy is transferred by the bulb over a time period of **5 minutes**.

....

....

iii) Calculate how much charge passes through the bulb in this time.

....

d) The sensor uses a **d.c.** electricity supply. Explain, in terms of charge carriers, what this means.

....

....

Stopping Distances

Q1   **Stopping distance** and **braking distance** are **not** the same thing.

a)   What is meant by 'braking distance'?

....

b)   Use the words below to complete the following sentences.

braking   noticing   react   thinking   hazard

i)   Thinking distance is the distance travelled in the time it takes a driver to ....

ii)   Reaction time is the time between a driver .... a ....
and applying the brakes.

iii) Stopping distance = ... distance + ... distance.

Q2   Will the following factors affect **thinking** distance, **braking** distance or **both**?
Write them in the relevant columns of the table.

tiredness   road surface   weather   speed   diesel spills
alcohol   tyre tread   brakes   mass of the vehicle   ice

Thinking Distance	Braking Distance

Q3   Beth wants to make a toy car race track. To help her decide which material to
use, she finds the **force** needed to slide a 1 kg rubber block across a flat surface
covered in three different materials. The table below shows her results.

a)   What force opposes the block sliding? ....

b)   Beth wants the toy cars to be able to grip well to the track.
Which of the surfaces tested should she use to make the race track?
Explain your answer.

Material .... because ....

....

Material	Force needed for block to slide
1	60 N
2	5 N
3	24 N

Q4   A car has just been driven through a **deep puddle**, making the brakes
wet. Explain why this will **increase** the **stopping distance** of the car.

....

....

Car Safety

Q1 Circle the correct words or phrases to make the following statements true.

a) If the velocity of a moving object doubles, its **kinetic energy** / **momentum** will double.

b) If you drop a suitcase out of a moving car, the car's momentum will **decrease** / **increase**.

c) When two objects collide the total momentum **changes** / **stays the same**.

d) When a force acts on an object its momentum **changes** / **stays the same**.

Q2 Place the following four trucks in order of increasing momentum.

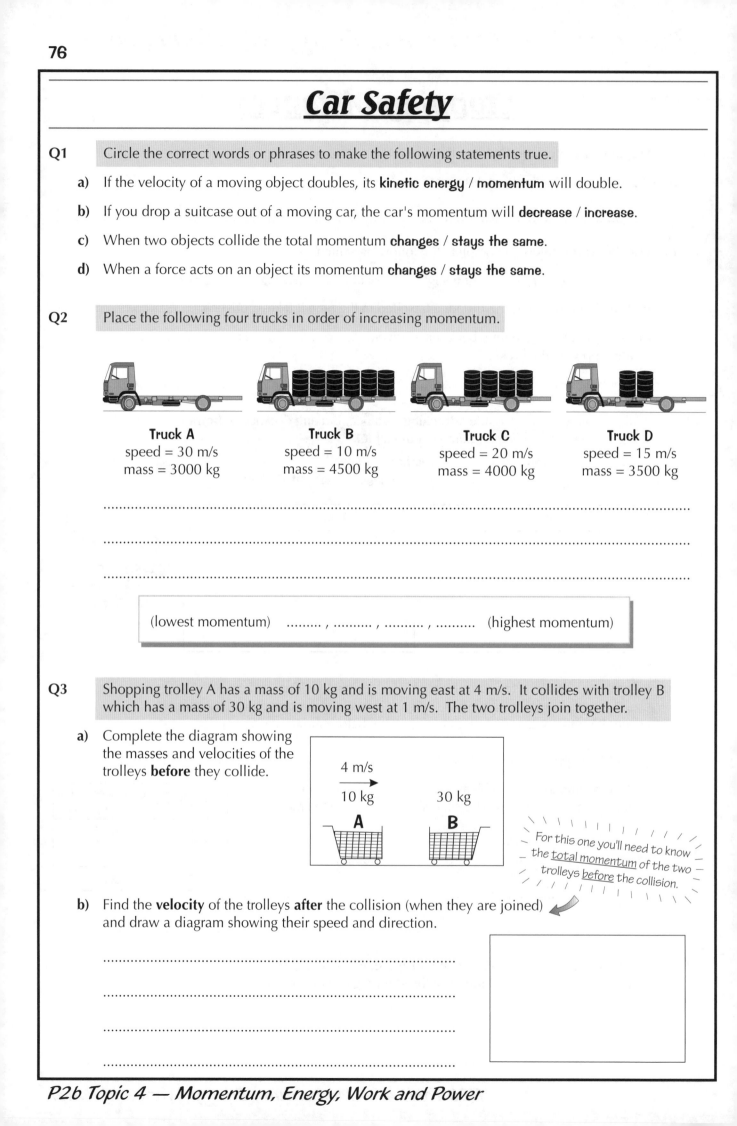

Truck A	Truck B	Truck C	Truck D
speed = 30 m/s	speed = 10 m/s	speed = 20 m/s	speed = 15 m/s
mass = 3000 kg	mass = 4500 kg	mass = 4000 kg	mass = 3500 kg

....

....

....

(lowest momentum)   .... , ... , ... , ...   (highest momentum)

Q3 Shopping trolley A has a mass of 10 kg and is moving east at 4 m/s. It collides with trolley B which has a mass of 30 kg and is moving west at 1 m/s. The two trolleys join together.

a) Complete the diagram showing the masses and velocities of the trolleys **before** they collide.

4 m/s

10 kg   30 kg

A   B

For this one you'll need to know the total momentum of the two trolleys before the collision.

b) Find the **velocity** of the trolleys **after** the collision (when they are joined) and draw a diagram showing their speed and direction.

....

....

....

....

P2b Topic 4 — Momentum, Energy, Work and Power

Car Safety

Q4 A 750 kg car is travelling at 30 m/s along the motorway. It crashes into the barrier of the central reservation and is stopped in a period of 1.2 seconds.

a) Find the size of the **average force** acting on the car to stop it.

....

....

b) Explain why the occupants of the car are likely to be less severely injured if they are wearing seat belts made of slightly **stretchy** material.

....

....

Q5 A 0.15 kg cricket ball is dropped vertically onto a floor. It hits the floor at a speed of 10 m/s and bounces vertically back up at the same speed. If the ball is in contact with the floor for 0.02 s, what is the average force exerted on it?

How does the ball's velocity change?

....

....

....

....

Q6 Simon is investigating **crumple zones** using the apparatus shown on the right.

Crumple zone • Trolley • Force sensor • To data logger • Smooth sloped surface

Simon fits the front of a trolley with different materials to make different 'crumple zones'. For each test, the trolley starts **at rest** at the **same position** on the slope and rolls towards the force sensor. The **mass** of the trolley is the **same** in each test. Simon records the **maximum force** of the trolley on the sensor, and **how long** each collision lasts for in the table below.

Crumple zone	Maximum force during the collision (N)	Collision time (s)
1	10	0.8
2	40	0.2
3	16	0.5

Which of Simon's crumple zones was the most effective? Explain your answer.

....

....

....

P2b Topic 4 — Momentum, Energy, Work and Power

Work and Power

Q1 Circle the correct words to make the following sentences true.

a) Work involves the transfer of **force** / **heat** / **energy**.

b) To do work **a force** / **an acceleration** must act over a **distance** / **time**.

c) Work is measured in **watts** / **joules**.

Q2 Indicate whether the following statements are **true** or **false**.

		True	False
a)	Work is done when a toy car is pushed along the ground.	☐	☐
b)	No work is done if a force is applied to an object which does not move.	☐	☐
c)	Gravity does work on an apple that is not moving.	☐	☐
d)	Gravity does work on an apple that falls out of a tree.	☐	☐

Q3 Complete this passage by using the words provided.

heat   energy   100   rate   light   watts   joules
Power is the .... of doing work, or how much .... is transferred per second. It is measured in .... or .... per second. A 100 W light bulb transfers .... joules of electrical energy into .... and .... each second.

Q4 An elephant exerts a constant force of **1200 N** to push a donkey along a track at a steady **1 m/s**.

a) Write down the equation that links force, distance and work done.

....

b) Calculate the work done by the elephant if the donkey moves **8 m**.

....

c) From where does the elephant get the energy to do this work? ....

d) Into what form(s) is this energy transferred when work is done on the donkey?

....

Top Tips: Power is a measure of the energy transferred, or work done, within a certain time — the faster a person or machine can get a task done, the more powerful it is. Just think, if you were a power-mad ruler you could try take over the world in the blink of an eye, mwah haa ha ha ha...

Work and Power

Q5 Ben's mass is 60 kg. He climbs a ladder. The rungs of the ladder are 20 cm apart.

a) What force(s) is Ben doing work **against** as he climbs?

....

b) As he climbs, what happens to the **energy** supplied by Ben's muscles?

....

....

20 cm

c) How much work does Ben do when he climbs **10 rungs**? (Ignore any 'wasted' energy.)
Assume that g = 10 N/kg.

....

....

d) How many rungs of the ladder must Ben climb before he has done **15 kJ** of work?
(Ignore any 'wasted' energy.) Assume that g = 10 N/kg.

....

....

Q6 Catherine and Sally decide to run up a set of stairs to see who can get to the top more quickly. At the top of the stairs, Catherine has a gravitational potential energy of **2300 J**, and Sally has a gravitational potential energy of **2400 J**.

Catherine won the race in **6.2 s**, while Sally took **6.4 s**.
Which girl generated more **power**?

....

....

Q7 Tom likes to build model boats. His favourite boat is the Carter, which has a motor power of **150 W**.

a) How much **energy** does the Carter transfer in **10 minutes**?

....

b) The petrol for the boat's motor can supply **30 kJ/ml**.
What volume of petrol is used up in **10 minutes**?

....

c) Tom decides to get a model speed boat which transfers **120 kJ** in 10 minutes.
What is the **power** of the engine?

....

Kinetic and Potential Energy

Q1 Indicate whether the following statements are **true** or **false**.

	True	False
a) Gravitational potential energy = mass × g × height.	☺	☹
b) Kinetic energy is energy due to an object's position.	☺	☹
c) On Earth, the gravitational field strength is approximately **20 N/kg**.	☺	☹
d) The kinetic energy of an object depends on its velocity.	☺	☹
e) Brakes convert kinetic energy into mostly heat energy to slow down a car.	☺	☹

Q2 Dave works at a DIY shop. He has to load **28** flagstones onto the delivery truck. Each flagstone has a mass of **25 kg** and has to be lifted **1.2 m** onto the truck.

a) How much gravitational potential energy does one flagstone gain when lifted onto the truck? (g = 10 N/kg)

....

b) What is the **total gravitational potential energy** gained by the flagstones after they are all loaded onto the truck?

....

Q3 A large truck and a car both have a kinetic energy of **614 400 J**. The mass of the truck is **12 288 kg** and the car **1200 kg**.

a) Calculate the **speed** of:

i) the car ....

ii) the truck ....

b) John is playing with his remote-controlled toy car and truck. The car's mass is 100 g. The truck's mass is 300 g. The car is moving twice as fast as the truck. Which has more kinetic energy — the car or the truck? Explain your answer.

....

....

Q4 Jack rides his bicycle along a level road and has a total kinetic energy of **1440 J**. He brakes, exerting a force of **200 N** on the wheels. How far does he travel before he stops?

....

Top Tips: My physics teacher once said I had lots of potential... thanks to being sat on an exceptionally tall stool. Ah, physics jokes... you've got to love 'em. Kinetic energy and gravitational potential energy crop up everywhere, so make sure you get friendly with their formulas.

Conservation of Energy

Q1 A toy cricket ball hit straight upwards has a gravitational potential energy of **242 J** at the **top** of its flight.

a) What is the ball's **kinetic energy just** before it hits the ground? ....

b) Calculate the speed of the ball at this time if its mass is **100 g**.

....

Q2 Mr Coles is about to demonstrate the **conservation of energy**. He holds a heavy pendulum up by a window and lets go.

a) Explain why he can be sure that the pendulum won't smash the window when it swings back.

....

....

b) When the pendulum actually does swing back, it doesn't quite reach the height of the window again. Where has the gravitational potential energy gone?

....

Q3 Dave the frog **jumps** off the ground at a speed of 10 m/s.

a) If Dave has a mass of 500 g, what is his kinetic energy as he leaves the ground?

....

b) What is Dave's maximum possible gravitational potential energy?

....

c) What is the maximum height Dave can reach?

....

d) In practice, why won't Dave reach this height? (Explain your answer in terms of energy.)

....

....

Q4 Kim dives off a **5 m** high diving board and belly-flops into the swimming pool below.

a) If Kim's mass is 100 kg, calculate her kinetic energy as she hits the water.

....

b) At what speed will Kim be falling as she hits the water?

....

Radioactivity

Q1 Fill in the blanks using the words below. Each word should be used only once.

alpha	element	protons	neutrons	nuclei	gamma	radioactive

Isotopes are atoms which have the same number of .... but different numbers of .... Some isotopes are .... Their ....

are unstable, so they break down and emit either .... , beta or

.... radiation. When isotopes break down in this way, the nucleus often

changes into that of a new ....

Q2 Indicate whether these sentences are **true** or **false**.

                                                                             True   False

a) The number of protons in an atom is known as its atomic number. ☐ ☐

b) The number of neutrons in an atom is known as its mass number. ☐ ☐

c) Atoms of the same element with the same number of neutrons are called isotopes. ☐ ☐

d) Radioactive decay speeds up at higher temperatures. ☐ ☐

Q3 For each of the following isotopes, state the **number of protons** and the **number of neutrons**.

a) $^{3}_{1}\text{H}$

b) $^{14}_{6}\text{C}$

c) $^{14}_{7}\text{N}$

d) $^{16}_{8}\text{O}$

Protons: ....   Protons: ....   Protons: ....   Protons: ....

Neutrons: ....   Neutrons: ....   Neutrons: ....   Neutrons: ....

Q4 An atom is bombarded with ionising radiation. **Explain** how the following could **ionise** the atom:

a) An **alpha** particle passing close by.

....

....

b) A **beta** particle passing close by.

....

....

Radioactivity

Q5 Complete the table below to show the properties of alpha, beta and gamma radiation.

Radiation Type	What is it?	Ionising power weak/moderate/ strong	Penetrating power low/moderate/ high
alpha			
beta			
gamma			

Q6 a) For each sentence, tick the correct box to show whether it is **true** or **false**.

True False

i) All nuclear radiation is positively charged. ☐ ☐

ii) Gamma radiation can pass through thin sheets of metal. ☐ ☐

iii) Alpha is the slowest and most strongly ionising type of radiation. ☐ ☐

iv) Beta particles are electrons, so they do not come from the nucleus. ☐ ☐

b) For each of the false sentences, write out a correct version.

....

....

....

Q7 Radiation from three sources — A, B and C, was directed towards target sheets of **paper**, **aluminium** and **lead**. Counters were used to detect where radiation passed through the target sheets.

Source A — the radiation was partially absorbed by the lead.
Source B — the radiation was stopped by the paper.
Source C — the radiation was stopped by the aluminium.

paper   3 mm aluminium   1 cm lead

A - - - - - - - - - - - - →
B - - - - - - - →
C · · · · · · · →

Radioactive sources

What type of radiation is emitted by:

source A? ...., source B? ...., source C? ....

84

<u>*Nuclear Fission*</u>

Q1   Many nuclear power stations split **uranium-235** nuclei in their reactors.

   a) **Daughter nuclei** such as barium and krypton are **products** of the fission of uranium-235.
Give **two other** products of the fission reaction.

   1. ....   2. ....

   b) Describe how a fission chain reaction is created in a nuclear reactor.

   ....

   ....

   ....

   ....

Q2   The diagram below shows how energy from a nuclear reactor generates electricity.

   a) Describe how heat energy from the reactor is used to generate electricity.

   ....

   ....

   b) What causes the reactor to get hot?

   ....

   c) What can be used in a nuclear reactor to slow down neutrons for nuclear fission?

   ....

   d) **i)** Explain how the control rods control the rate of fission.

   ....

   ....

   ii) What material are control rods usually made from? ....

   e) What could happen if the chain reaction in a nuclear reactor wasn't checked and controlled?

   ....

   ....

P2b Topic 5 — Nuclear Fission and Nuclear Fusion

Nuclear Fusion

Q1 Decide whether the following statements are **true** or **false**.
Write out the correct version of any false statements.

	True	False
	☐	☐
	☐	☐
	☐	☐
	☐	☐

a) Nuclear fusion involves small nuclei joining together.

b) A nuclear fission reaction releases more energy than a nuclear fusion reaction.

c) Fusion reactors produce very little radioactive waste.

d) Only a few experimental fusion reactors are generating electricity.

....

....

Q2 The energy released in stars comes from fusion.

a) **i)** Write down two conditions needed for fusion to take place.

1. .... 2. ....

ii) Explain why these extreme conditions are necessary.

....

b) Fusion reactors are extremely hard to build.

i) Why can the hydrogen used not be held in a physical container?

....

ii) How do fusion reactors get around this problem?

....

c) Describe the main problem with the amount of energy a fusion reactor needs to operate.

....

Q3 In 1989 two scientists claimed to have created energy through **cold fusion**.

a) In what ways did they say cold fusion was different from previous ideas about nuclear fusion?

....

b) Explain why the theory has not been accepted by the scientific community.

....

....

....

....

Background Radiation and Half-life

Q1 Use the words in the box to fill in the gaps in the paragraph below.

becquerels	half-life	decreases	zero
second	undecayed		Geiger-Muller

The activity of a radioactive source .... over time as the radioactive

nuclei decay. However, the activity never reaches .... , so scientists

use the idea of .... to measure how quickly the activity falls. This is

the time it takes for half the .... nuclei in a radioactive substance to

decay. Activity is measured in .... — 1 Bq is one decay per

.... , which can be measured using a .... tube.

Q2 Which of the following are **true**? Circle the appropriate letters.

A About half of the UK's background radiation comes from radon gas.

B Human activity doesn't contribute to background radiation.

C If there were no radioactive substances on Earth, there would be no background radiation.

D Cosmic rays from the Sun are a form of low-level background radiation.

Q3 The concentration of **radon** gas found in people's homes varies across the UK.
Why does the concentration vary across the country?

....

....

Q4 A radioactive isotope has a half-life of **60 years**.
Which of these statements describes this isotope correctly? Tick one box only.

In 60 years, half of the atoms in the material will have gone. ☐

In 30 years' time, only half the atoms will be radioactive. ☐

In 60 years' time, the activity will be half what it is now. ☐

In about 180 years there will be almost no radioactivity left in the material. ☐

Q5 The half-life of uranium-238 is **4500 million** years. The half-life of carbon-14 is **5730** years.
If you start with a sample of each element and the two samples have equal initial activity,
which will lose its radioactivity most quickly? Circle the correct answer.

uranium-238   carbon-14

Calculating Half-life

Q1 The graph shows how the activity of a radioactive isotope declines with time.

Activity (Bq) vs Time (minutes)

a) What is the half-life of this isotope?

....

b) What was the activity after 3 half-lives?

....

c) What fraction of the original radioactive nuclei will still be unstable after 5 half-lives?

....

d) After how long was the activity down to 100 Bq?

....

Q2 Dice can be used to simulate **radioactive decay**. 24 dice each represent an unstable isotope that could decay at any moment. The dice are rolled and any which roll a six are removed — they have "**decayed**". The remaining dice are rolled again, and so on, until all the dice have decayed.

Describe one way in which this experiment accurately models radioactive decay.

....

....

Q3 A radioactive isotope has a half-life of **40 seconds**.

You'll need to change 6 minutes into seconds.

a) What fraction of the unstable nuclei will still be radioactive after 6 minutes?

....

....

b) i) If the initial activity of the sample was 8000 Bq, what would be the approximate activity after 6 minutes?

....

....

ii) After how many whole **minutes** would the activity have fallen below 10 Bq?

....

....

Uses of Radioactivity

Q1   Complete the following paragraph using the words provided.

ill	minimised	normal	kill	cells	cancer

High doses of gamma radiation will .... living ....

Because of this, gamma radiation is used to treat .... Damage to

.... cells can make the patient feel very ....

This damage is .... by directing the radiation at the tumour.

Q2   The table shows some commonly used radioactive isotopes and the type of radiation they emit.

a)   Which of these isotopes would be most
suitable for these applications?

    i) A smoke detector.

    ....

    ii) To irradiate pre-packed food.

    ....

Radioactive isotope	Decays by...
strontium-90	beta emission
americium-241	mainly alpha emission
cobalt-60	beta and gamma emission

b)   What further information about these isotopes would you want before you considered using them?

....

....

Q3   The following sentences explain how a smoke detector works, but they are in the wrong order.

Put them in order by labelling them 1 (first) to 5 (last).

☐   The circuit is broken so no current flows.

1   The radioactive source emits alpha particles.

☐   The alarm sounds.

☐   A fire starts and smoke particles absorb the alpha radiation.

☐   The alpha particles cause ionisation of the air
between two electrodes and a current flows.

Top Tips: When you're answering questions about the uses of radioactivity, it's important
that you remember the properties of the different types of ionising radiation. Each of the three
types can be dangerous if used incorrectly, but pretty darned useful in the right scenario.

Uses of Radioactivity

Q4 The diagram shows how **beta radiation** can be used in the control of paper thickness in a paper mill.

Why is beta radiation used rather than alpha or gamma?

....

....

....

Q5 Radiation can be used to **sterilise** surgical instruments.

a) What kind of radioactive source is used, and why? In your answer, mention the **type** of radiation emitted (alpha, beta and gamma) and the **half-life** of the source.

....

....

....

b) What is the purpose of the **thick lead**?

....

c) Similar machines can be used to treat **fruit** before it is exported from South America to Europe, to stop it going bad on the long journey. How does irradiating the fruit help?

....

....

Q6 There will often be an **increased** blood flow to the part of the body where there is a cancerous tumour.

a) Describe how a radioactive tracer can be used to diagnose medical problems such as cancer.

....

....

....

b) What should the **half-life** of the radioactive isotope used in the tracer be, and what **type** of radiation should it emit? Explain your answers.

....

....

....

<u>*Dangers of Radioactivity*</u>

Q1 The three different types of ionising radiation can all be dangerous.

a) Which **two** types of ionising radiation can pass through the human body?
Circle the correct answers.

alpha   beta   gamma

b) i) Which type of radiation is usually most dangerous if it's inhaled or swallowed?

....

ii) What effects can this type of radiation have on the human body?

....

....

....

Q2 Give **four precautions** you should take when working with **radioactive sources** in the laboratory.

1. ....

2. ....

3. ....

4. ....

Q3 When the radioactive substance **radium** was first discovered, it was used to make luminous paint, which was used in the manufacture of glow-in-the-dark watches.

a) Explain why this was **extremely dangerous** to the watch painters.

....

....

b) The use of radium in a range of products went on for over **20 years**.
Explain why its use continued for so long.

....

....

....

Nuclear Power

Q1   The majority of the UK's electricity is still produced by burning **fossil fuels**.

a)   Is generating electricity using nuclear power a cheaper alternative to using fossil fuels?
Explain your answer.

....

....

b)   Write down **two** other **advantages** and **disadvantages** of nuclear power
compared to using fossil fuels to generate electricity.

Advantages: 1. ....

2. ....

Disadvantages: 1. ....

2. ....

c)   Explain why some people are **against** the use of nuclear power to generate our electricity.

....

....

....

Q2   **Radioactive waste** left over from **nuclear fission** is very difficult to dispose of.

a)   Why is the waste produced by nuclear power stations such a long-term problem?

....

....

b)   Vitrification is one way of disposing of radioactive waste.
Describe the process of vitrification.

....

....

c)   Why is nuclear waste usually buried deep underground?

....

....

Top Tips: Nuclear power is a tricky subject — there are arguments for and against it.
Make sure you know **both** sides of the argument. That way you can argue with yourself.

Mixed Questions — P2b Topics 4, 5 & 6

Q1   Nick and Rob go on a roller coaster. With them in it, the
roller coaster carriage has a total mass of **1200 kg**.

   a)   At the start of the ride the carriage rises up to its highest point of **60 m**
above the ground and stops. Calculate its gain in gravitational potential energy.

   ....

   ....

   b)   The carriage then falls to a third of its maximum height. Assuming there is no air resistance or
friction, calculate the speed of the carriage at this point.

   ....

   ....

   ....

   c)   One of the carriages needs to be repaired. A super strong handyman pushes
it 120 m from the ride to the repair workshop. Calculate the work done
by the handyman, if he pushes the carriage with a constant force of 85 N.

   ....

   ....

Q2   The table gives information about four different **radioactive isotopes**.

   a)   Explain how the atomic structure of cobalt-60 ($^{60}_{27}$Co) is
different from the structure of 'normal' cobalt-59 ($^{59}_{27}$Co).

Source	Type of Radiation	Half-life
radon-222	alpha	3.8 days
technetium-99m	gamma	6 hours
americium-241	alpha	432 years
cobalt-60	beta and gamma	5.27 years

   ....

   ....

   b)   Which sources in the table would be
most suitable for each of the uses below?

   ....
   medical tracers   **smoke detectors**   **detecting leaks in pipes**

   c)   Radiation can be used to treat cancer. What type of radiation is used in this treatment?

   ....

   d)   Give **one** precaution that should be taken by industrial nuclear
workers to protect themselves from radiation.

   ....

Mixed Questions — P2b Topics 4, 5 & 6

Q3   The diagram below shows part of a chain reaction in a nuclear reactor.

a) What is the name of the type of nuclear reaction shown in the diagram?

....

b) This decay happens as part of a chain reaction. Describe what happens in this chain reaction.

....

....

....

c) Explain how the following work to control the chain reaction in a nuclear reactor.

    i) Moderators: ....

       ....

    ii) Control rods: ....

       ....

d) What would happen if this reaction was not controlled?

....

....

e) Describe how thermal energy from the reactor is used to generate electricity.

....

....

f) Give one disadvantage of using nuclear power to generate electricity compared to other methods.

....

g) Nuclear **fusion** produces more energy than the process above.
Write down one of the conditions needed for fusion to take place.

....

Mixed Questions — P2b Topics 4, 5 & 6

Q4 Cherie and Tony rob a bank. They escape in a getaway car with a mass of **2100 kg** and travel at a constant speed of **90 km/h** along a straight, level road.

a) Calculate the momentum of the car.

....

....

b) A police car swings into the middle of the road and stops ahead of Cherie's car. Cherie slams on the brakes and comes to a halt **3.0 s** after she starts braking.

  i) Write down one factor that could affect Cherie's thinking distance.

  ....

  ii) Assuming the car decelerates uniformly, find the force acting on the braking car.

  ....

  ....

  ....

c) Explain how seat belts would have helped keep Cherie and Tony safer if they had crashed.

....

....

Q5 Fay measures the activity of a sample of pure copper-64 in her home, using a Geiger-Muller tube. The graph below shows her results.

a) Fay had previously measured the background rate to be 100 Bq. Find the half-life of copper-64.

....

....

....

....

....

b) She takes her Geiger-Muller tube to her friend's house and finds the background rate is much higher. Give one reason why the level of background radiation changes from place to place.

....

Medical Physics and Ultrasound

Q1 In each of the following sentences, circle the correct word(s) from each highlighted pair.

a) X-rays are **low / high** energy electromagnetic waves.

b) X-rays are **transmitted / absorbed** by soft tissue but are
transmitted / absorbed by dense material such as bone.

c) X-rays are a type of **ionising / non-ionising** radiation.

Q2 Tick the boxes to show whether each of these statements is **true** or **false**.

		True	False
a)	CAT scans can produce an image of a 2-D 'slice' of the body.	☐	☐
b)	Only soft tissue can be imaged by CAT scans.	☐	☐
c)	CAT scans use ultrasound waves.	☐	☐
d)	Ionising radiation is used to produce a CAT scan.	☐	☐
e)	CAT scans are typically used to check fetal development.	☐	☐

Q3 A concentrated beam of **ultrasound** can be used to treat kidney stones.

a) What is ultrasound?

....

....

b) What effect does the ultrasound beam have on kidney stones?

....

c) How are the kidney stone remains removed from the body?

....

d) Give two reasons why using ultrasound is a good way of treating kidney stones.

1. ....

2. ....

e) Describe **one** other medical use of ultrasound.

....

....

Intensity of Radiation

Q1 The word '**radiation**' is often used to refer to nuclear sources, but it also covers many other types.

a) Sort the following forms of radiation according to their properties.

neutron

visible light

gamma

alpha

X-rays

beta

(Venn diagram with three overlapping circles labelled "Electromagnetic", "Ionising", and "Particle")

b) What is the definition of radiation?

....

Q2 Tick the boxes to show whether each of these statements is **true** or **false**.

	True	False
a) The intensity of radiation depends on the medium it has passed through.	☐	☐
b) A vacuum absorbs some of the radiation passing through it.	☐	☐
c) Generally, the less dense the medium, the more radiation that is absorbed.	☐	☐

Q3 Sam and Amy have made a spherical lantern for the Halloween parade. The lantern has a **diameter** of **40 cm** and contains a candle with a power of **0.8 W** at its centre.

a) Calculate the surface area of the lantern, in square metres.

Remember the surface area of a sphere $= 4/3\,\pi\,r^2$

....

....

b) Calculate the **intensity** of the light radiation on the inside surface of the lantern.

....

c) How will the intensity of the light from the candle reaching the outside surface of the lantern compare to that reaching the inside surface? Explain your answer.

....

....

Top Tips: If this intensity of radiation malarkey is just not making sense, try getting a torch out and seeing it in action. Hold your hand up close to the torch, what do you see — a bright spot of light. Shine it on the fence at the bottom of the garden, guess what — a large patch of dim light.

P3a Topic 1 — Radiation and Treatment

Lenses

Q1   Fill in the blanks in the passage below.

> Waves can speed up or .... when they
>
> pass from one medium to another. If they are travelling at an angle
>
> to the .... then the change in speed results
>
> in a change of ....

Q2   The diagram shows a ray of light passing across the **boundary** between two media.

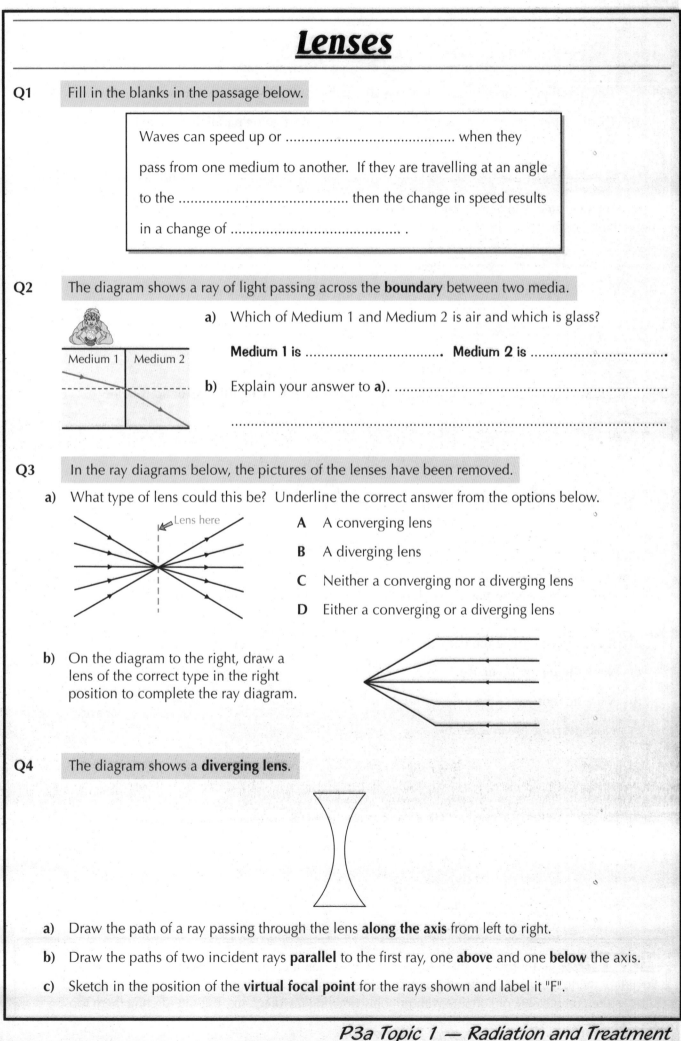

a)   Which of Medium 1 and Medium 2 is air and which is glass?

Medium 1 is .... **Medium 2 is** ....

b)   Explain your answer to **a**). ....

....

Q3   In the ray diagrams below, the pictures of the lenses have been removed.

a)   What type of lens could this be? Underline the correct answer from the options below.

Lens here

A   A converging lens

B   A diverging lens

C   Neither a converging nor a diverging lens

D   Either a converging or a diverging lens

b)   On the diagram to the right, draw a lens of the correct type in the right position to complete the ray diagram.

Q4   The diagram shows a **diverging lens**.

a)   Draw the path of a ray passing through the lens **along the axis** from left to right.

b)   Draw the paths of two incident rays **parallel** to the first ray, one **above** and one **below** the axis.

c)   Sketch in the position of the **virtual focal point** for the rays shown and label it "F".

<u>Lenses</u>

Q5 This question is about how to **draw ray diagrams** to show an image formed by a **converging** lens.

a) The first step is to draw a ray from the **top** of the object going **parallel** to the **axis** of the lens. Where does this ray pass through when it's refracted?

....

b) The next step is to draw a ray from the top of the object which passes through the lens **without** being refracted. Where does this ray pass through the lens?

....

c) How do the steps above tell you where the **top** of the **image** will be on the ray diagram?

....

Q6 Draw a ray diagram to locate where the image is by **following the instructions** below.

a) Draw a ray from the **top** of the object (towards the lens) **parallel** to the axis, and continue the path of the ray through the lens.

b) Draw a ray from the top of the object passing through the **centre** of the lens.

c) Mark the **top** of the image.

d) Mark the **bottom** of the image, and draw in the image.

Take these ray diagrams step by step. Make sure you draw them really carefully, with a <u>ruler</u>.

e) Now **describe** the image fully.

....

....

....

....

<u>Top Tips:</u> There are a lot of technical terms when it comes to lenses and ray diagrams — 'inverted', 'virtual image' and 'focal point' to name just a few. Take your time over these pages and make sure you're completely comfortable with not only drawing ray diagrams, but interpreting them too.

Lenses

Q7   Complete this ray diagram so that you can **fully describe** the image that this lens produces.

Description of image: ....

....

....

Q8   An aubergine is placed 6.1 cm away from a converging lens with a focal length of **7 cm**.

a)   Will the image formed by the lens be:

   i)   upright or inverted? ....

   ii) on the same side of the lens or on the opposite side? ....

   iii) real or virtual? ....

b)   The aubergine is now placed at a distance X from the lens. The image is now bigger than the object and inverted. Which of the options below could be distance X? Circle your answer.

   A 3.9 cm   **B** 7.0 cm   **C** 10.2 cm   **D** 14.0 cm   **E** 15.3 cm

Q9   Circle the correct options in this description of images formed by **diverging lenses**.

   Diverging lenses always produce **real** / **virtual**, **upright** / **inverted**

   images which are **smaller** / **larger** than the object.

Q10   The diagram below shows an object placed next to a diverging lens. The focal points are marked.

object

F   F axis

a)   On the diagram, draw the path of a ray coming from the top of the object and travelling in the direction of the centre of the lens.

b)   Draw the path of a ray coming from the top of the object and going towards the focal point on the far side of the lens.

c)   Draw the image formed by the lens.

Power and the Lens Equation

Q1   Dave is using a converging lens to **focus** some parallel rays of light to a point.

a)   If the distance between the centre of the lens, X, and the focal point, Y, is 15 cm, what is the power of the lens?

....

b)   Dave wants to increase the distance between the lens and the focal point, so he switches the lens for one with a power of +5.2 D. Calculate the new distance between X and Y.

....

....

c)   Assuming they are made of the same material, how will the lens Dave uses in part **b)** look different to the one in part **a)**?

....

Q2   The **lens equation** can be used to find the position of an image created by a **converging lens**.

a)   i)   Write the lens equation that links the letters f, v and u.

....

   ii)   Write down what the letters f, v and u stand for in the equation you wrote in **a) i)**.

   f = ... v = ... u = ...

b)   An armadillo squats **0.5 m** from a converging lens of focal length **0.6 m**.

   i)   Use the lens equation to calculate the **distance** of the **image** of the armadillo from the lens.

....

....

....

   ii)   **Describe** the image of the armadillo.

....

....

The Eye

Q1 Write **labels** in the spaces to complete the diagram of a human eye.

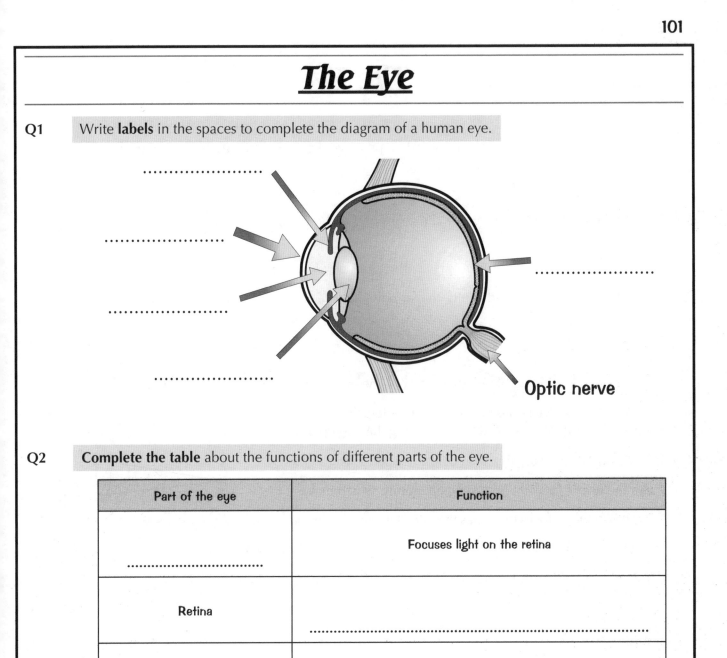

....

....

....

....

....

Optic nerve

Q2 **Complete the table** about the functions of different parts of the eye.

Part of the eye	Function
....	Focuses light on the retina
Retina	....
Ciliary muscles	....
....	Hole through which light enters the eye

Q3 Circle the correct word in each pair to complete the passage below.

> When you look at distant objects, your ciliary muscles **contract** / **relax**,
>
> and pull the lens to make it **thin** / **fat**. The opposite actions happen when
>
> you look at near objects. The combined action of the lens and **cornea** / **iris**
>
> focuses the light on the **pupil** / **retina** to produce an image. Cells on the
>
> **pupil** / **retina** send signals to the brain to be interpreted via the optic nerve.

The Eye

Q4 The range of human eyesight lies between the **near** and **far points**.
Complete the definitions of near and far points and give an **estimated value** for each.

a) i) The near point is ....

ii) For normally-sighted adults, the near point is about .... cm.

b) i) The far point is ....

ii) For normally-sighted adults, the far point is at ....

Q5 Common vision problems are caused by the eye focusing an image in the wrong place.

a) Look at the diagram on the right. Complete the sentences by
circling the correct word(s) from the highlighted options.

This person, with this vision defect, is **short / long** sighted.

The **near / far** point is closer than infinity, which makes

it difficult to focus on things that are **close up / far away**.

object

The object in the diagram is brought into focus **in front of / behind** the retina.

b) Give **two possible causes** of the problem shown in the diagram.

1. ....

2. ....

Q6 James has just been diagnosed as **long-sighted**.

a) i) Describe how being long-sighted affects James' near point.

....

ii) A correctly focused eye will form an image of near and far objects exactly on the retina.
Where will James' eyes form a focused image of a nearby object?

....

b) Give two possible **causes** of James' long sight.

1. ....

2. ....

Correcting Vision Defects

Q1 Short sight can be corrected by placing a lens in front of the cornea.

a) Which of the two lenses shown below could correct this problem? Circle the correct letter.

A   B

b) Explain how the lens you chose in part **a)** would help to correct the eye problem.

....

....

....

Q2 Lasers are used in corrective **eye surgery**.

a) Describe how can a laser be used to correct long sight.

....

....

b) Laser eye surgery is becoming an increasingly popular way to correct vision problems.

i) Give one advantage of having laser eye surgery to correct vision instead of using glasses.

....

ii) Describe two disadvantages of using laser correction instead of glasses to correct vision.

1. ....

....

2. ....

....

c) Name **one other way** in which long sight could be corrected.
Explain how this method of correction works.

....

....

Top Tips: Long sight is something that a lot of people suffer from as they get older. Once you get beyond the age of around 40, the lenses in your eyes get stiffer and lose their ability to change shape to become fat enough to focus on things close up. That's why a lot of older people need glasses to read — their lenses don't have the flexibility to focus on the words.

Snell's Law and Total Internal Reflection

Q1   Here is a diagram of a ray of light entering a material with **refractive index, n**.

air
(refractive index = 1)

material with
refractive index = n

a) Label the following parts of the diagram:

Incident ray   Normal   Refracted ray

Angle of incidence, i   Angle of refraction, r

b) Snell's law relates the refractive index, **n** to the two angles **i** and **r**. Write down Snell's law.

....

Q2   A light ray was shone from air into some water. The ray had an **angle of incidence** of **30°** and an **angle of refraction** of **22°**. Use this data to calculate the **refractive index** of water.

....

....

Q3   Optical fibres work because of repeated **total internal reflections**.

a) Complete the **ray diagrams** below. The critical angle for glass/air is **42°**.

You'll need to measure the angle of incidence for each one — carefully.

air

glass

air

glass

air

glass

b) What two conditions are essential for **total internal reflection** to occur?

1. ....

2. ....

c) Describe an **experiment** to find the critical angle of a **glass/air boundary** using the **equipment pictured on the right**.

Laser Pen

Glass Prism

....

....

....

....

....

....

P3a Topic 1 — Radiation and Treatment

Uses of Total Internal Reflection

Q1 Choose from the words below to complete the passage.

reflected	internal	diffraction	dense	core

Optical fibres depend on total .... reflection for their operation.

Visible light is sent down the cable and is .... when it hits the boundary

between the .... of the fibre and the less .... outer case.

Q2 The diagrams show rays of light in an **optical fibre**.
Draw arrows to match each diagram to the correct description of what is happening.

Total internal reflection

Most of the light passes
out of the optical fibre, but
some is reflected internally.

Most of the light is reflected
internally, but some emerges
along the surface of the glass.

Q3 What is meant by the 'critical angle' for a material?

....

....

Q4 Doctors use **endoscopes** to look inside patients' bodies. Endoscopes work using **optical fibres**.

a) What **material** could the optical fibres
in an endoscope be made from?

....

Light
source

Endoscope

b) Explain why doctors try not to
bend an endoscope sharply.

....

....

....

Uses of Total Internal Reflection

Q5 Light passes through the acrylic bottom of a boat into the water below. For blue light, the refractive index of **acrylic** is **1.498** (to 3 d.p.) and the refractive index of **water** is **1.337** (to 3 d.p.)

a) i) What happens to the **speed** of the light as it passes into the water?

....

ii) Complete this sentence by underlining the correct option.

The angle of refraction is **greater than** / **less than** the angle of incidence.

b) If the angle of incidence were equal to the critical angle, what would the **angle** of **refraction** be?

....

c) What happens to light which enters the water at an angle **greater** than the critical angle?

....

....

d) Calculate the **critical angle** for the **acrylic to water** boundary for blue light, to the nearest degree.

You'll need the equation with sin C in it.

....

....

....

Q6 The diagram shows the use of an **endoscope** in **keyhole surgery**.

a) Explain what is meant by the term **keyhole surgery**.

....

....

b) Outline how an **endoscope** works.

....

....

c) List two **advantages** of keyhole surgery over conventional surgery.

1. ....

2. ....

Electron Beams

Q1 The **current** carried by a beam of electrons is **4 mA**.

a) What is current a measure of?

....

b) How many **electrons** pass a certain point in the beam per second?

....

For this question, use $q = 1.6 \times 10^{-19}$ C.

....

Q2 An **electron** accelerates across a potential difference (voltage) of 4 kV. The charge on the electron is -1.6×10^{-19} C.

a) Calculate the **kinetic energy** gained by the electron.

....

b) How much **potential energy** will the electron lose?

....

Think about energy conservation.

Q3 The diagram to the right shows a machine for taking **dental X-rays**.

a) The filament is heated so that it **emits** electrons. What is the name of this process?

....

b) Sketch in and label the **path of the electron beam** on the diagram. Show the direction of the beam.

c) Sketch in and label the **path of the X-rays** on the diagram. Show the direction of the beam.

d) Why does the **electron beam** move from cathode to the anode?

....

....

e) At the **anode** the electrons from the beam strike atoms of the metal, causing them to emit **X-rays**. Where does the energy for the X-rays come from?

....

f) The equipment is contained in an **evacuated** glass tube, surrounded by lead casing. Explain why the glass case is evacuated.

An evacuated tube means a tube that contains a vacuum.

....

....

X-ray Intensity and Absorption

Q1   Explain why X-rays are highly **ionising**, in terms of their **energy** and **frequency**.

....

....

....

Q2   After falling off his skateboard, Tony goes to hospital to see if any of the bones in his hand are broken. A radiographer takes an **X-ray** photograph of his hand.

a) Use the words below to fill in the blanks to explain why the radiographer stands far away from the X-ray machine during Tony's X-ray.

four	intensity	eight	inverse	three

If the radiographer moves twice as far from the **X-ray** source, the same radiation

from the source is spread over .... times the area.

So the radiographer only receives $\dfrac{1}{2^2} = \dfrac{1}{4}$ of the intensity of the radiation.

This relationship is known as the .... square law.

b) The X-ray tube used to produce the X-rays is contained within a **lead casing**.

The graph below shows how the **intensity** of the X-rays passing **through** the casing changes depending on the **thickness** of the lead.

Use the graph to describe the **relationship** between the **absorption** of the X-rays passing through the lead and its **thickness**.

....

....

....

....

....

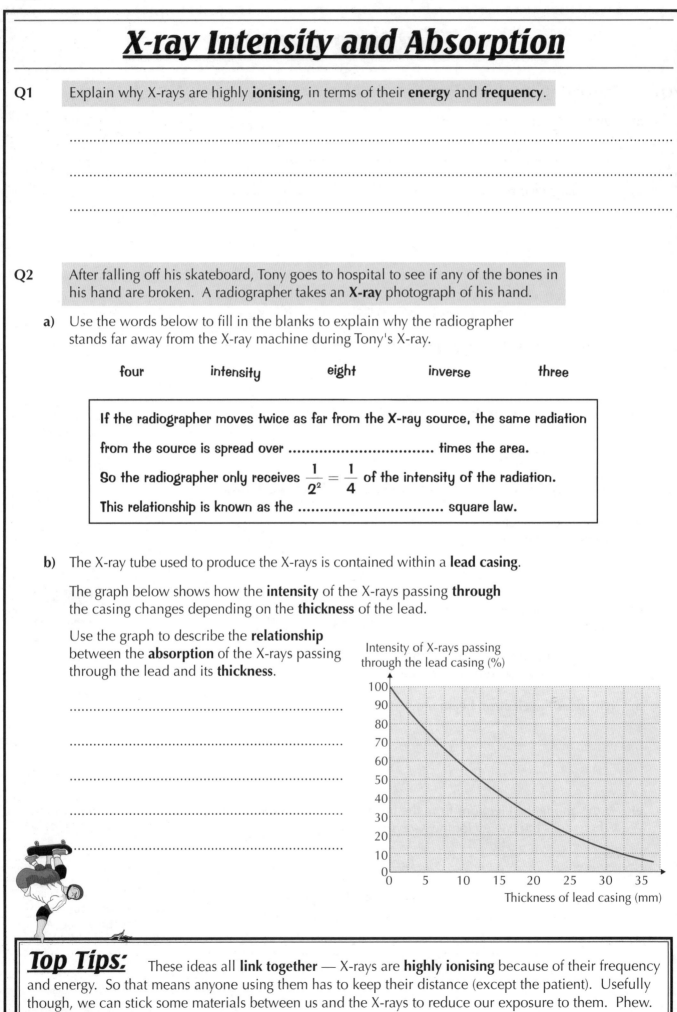

Intensity of X-rays passing through the lead casing (%)

Thickness of lead casing (mm)

Top Tips: These ideas all **link together** — X-rays are **highly ionising** because of their frequency and energy. So that means anyone using them has to keep their distance (except the patient). Usefully though, we can stick some materials between us and the X-rays to reduce our exposure to them. Phew.

X-ray Imaging

Q1 Tick the boxes to show whether each of these statements is **true** or **false**.

True False

a) Gamma rays are used in computerised axial tomography (CAT) scans. ☐ ☐

b) CAT scans produce low resolution images. ☐ ☐

c) CAT scans can be used to treat tumours and cancers. ☐ ☐

d) CAT scans can be used to produce 3-D images of the body. ☐ ☐

Q2 Fluoroscopes use X-rays to create **moving images** of patients' insides.

Choose from the words given below to complete the passage about how **fluoroscopes** work.

| intensity | fluoresces | fluorescent | brighter | passed | between | recorded |

A patient is placed .... an X-ray source and a ....

screen. The .... of X-rays reaching the screen depends on what they've

.... through in the body. The X-rays hit the screen which absorbs them

and .... (gives off light) to show a live image on a screen. The higher

the intensity of the X-rays, the .... the screen.   The screen is attached to

a computer so the images can be ....

Q3 Both **X-rays** and **ultrasound** can be used to image the inside of the body.

a) Use the words below to help you briefly describe **how X-rays** are used in **CAT** scans.

beam   rotates   detectors   computer   absorbed   image

....

....

....

....

b) Give **one** advantage of using ultrasound over CAT scans.

....

c) Give **one** reason why X-rays, rather than ultrasound, might be used to create an image of a patient.

....

d) Suggest a reason why X-rays are often used to diagnose a patient's medical condition, even though they're potentially harmful.

....

Electricity and the Body

Q1 A machine can be used to detect small **electrical signals** in a patient's muscles. These results can be used to **identify** problems with the muscles.

a) Define the following terms:

   i) resting potential ....

   ....

   ii) action potential ....

   ....

b) What value would you expect to record from a **contracted** muscle cell in a healthy person?

....

Q2 Electrocardiographs are used to measure the activity of the **heart**.

a) Describe, briefly, the **structure** of the heart.

....

b) Describe how a series of electrical signals help to produce a heart beat.

....

....

c) Describe the sensors used to detect the action potentials of a patient's heart.

....

Q3 The diagram below shows a typical **ECG** (electrocardiogram).

a) Show the size of the **resting potential** with an arrow on the y-axis.

b) What is the **period** of the heartbeat? ....

c) Calculate the frequency of the heartbeat in **beats per minute.**

....

d) What **muscle action** in the heart is being recorded at points:

   i) P ....

   ii) QRS ....

   iii) T ....

Top Tips: With a title like "Electricity and the Body", this page had so much potential. Chortle. Learn the shape of a normal ECG and know how all the different parts relate to the action of the heart.

Pace Makers and Pulse Oximeters

Q1   The diagram to the right shows a **pulse oximeter** on a hospital patient's **finger**.

a)   Add arrows to the diagram to show the direction of the red light and infrared beams.

b)   Choose from the words given below to complete the passage about how a pulse oximeter works.

reflected	reduced	absorbed	calibrated	monkey	tissue	increased

Red and infrared light pass through the .... and are detected by a

photo detector. Some of the light is .... by the red blood so that

the amount of light detected by the detector is .... The amount of

light absorbed depends on the amount of oxyhaemoglobin in the blood so the display can

be .... to show the blood's oxyhaemoglobin content.

c)   State one other suitable part of the **body** where a pulse oximeter could be placed. Explain your answer.

....

....

Q2   Arthur has been diagnosed with a **heart problem**. He is being fitted with an artificial **pacemaker** under the skin near his collarbone.

Briefly describe the function of a pacemaker and how it works.

....

....

....

Q3   **Reflection** pulse oximetry is used to measure the amount of oxygen in the blood.

a)   How does reflection pulse oximetry differ from the type of pulse oximetry described in question **1**?

....

b)   Connect the boxes below to complete the sentences about haemoglobin.

Oxyhaemoglobin is...   ...purply coloured...   ...and doesn't contain much oxygen.

Reduced haemoglobin is...   ...bright red...   ...and rich in oxygen.

Mixed Questions — P3a Topics 1 & 2

Q1 Karen has hurt her foot playing football. She is having an **X-ray** to find out whether she has broken a bone.

a) The X-rays have an **intensity** of 430 W/m². The surface area of Karen's foot is 0.024 m². Calculate the approximate **power** of the radiation reaching Karen's foot.

....

b) What does '**radiation**' mean?

....

c) Karen is given special glasses to wear while the X-ray is taken. Explain why.

....

....

d) The radiographer goes behind a lead screen while Karen has her X-ray. Why does he does this?

....

Q2 Nurse Horton uses a **pulse oximeter** to monitor the blood oxygen content of a patient who has recently had surgery.

a) Describe and explain how a pulse oximeter works.

....

....

....

b) If the blood has a high oxygen content, what colour will the oxyhaemoglobin appear?

....

Q3 **Ultrasound** is used in pre-natal scanning.

a) Briefly describe **how** ultrasound is used to form an image of a foetus.

....

....

b) Explain why ultrasound is used in pre-natal scanning rather than X-rays.

....

....

c) Give **two** other medical uses of ultrasound.

1. .... 2. ....

Mixed Questions — P3a Topics 1 & 2

Q4 James' doctor thinks he may have a cancerous tumour in his intestine. The surgeon decides to investigate further using **keyhole surgery**.

a) Name the **instrument** the surgeon would use to see inside James' body. ....

b) The instrument contains **optical fibres** to carry light into James' body and an image back out. Describe how light is carried along an optical fibre.

....

....

....

c) During the operation James is connected to an **ECG** machine to monitor the activity of his heart.

i) What does an ECG measure?

....

ii) Sketch the shape of a typical ECG on the axes provided. Label the components of the curve.

d) The time from peak to peak on James' ECG is **0.75 s**. Calculate the frequency of his heart beat.

....

Q5 Andrew and Cassie are looking at a shell. They can see it because images **form on their retinas**.

a) Complete the paths of the light rays on the diagram below for an eye with normal sight.

b) The light entering Cassie's eye is shown in the diagram to the right. Her lens is working correctly.

Circle the correct words to complete the sentences below.

Cassie's eyeball is too long / short, so images form behind / in front of her retina.

This can be corrected by diverging / converging spectacle lenses which make light rays come together.

c) Andrew uses a **magnifying glass** to examine the shell. He finds that to see a magnified image of the shell, the right way up, he must hold the lens less than 3 cm from it.

What is the focal length of this lens? ....

Mixed Questions — P3a Topics 1 & 2

Q6 Deirdre is long-sighted. She wears glasses to correct her vision.

a) The lens for her right eye has a focal length of **0.4 m**.

   i) Calculate the **power** of the lens.

....

....

   ii) The lens for her left eye is made of the **same material** as the lens for her right eye, but has a **higher power**. Describe how the two lenses will differ in appearance.

....

b) Deirdre is considering undergoing **laser eye** surgery to **correct** her vision.

   i) Give **one** possible risk associated with laser correction.

....

   ii) Suggest **one** other way she could correct her sight.

....

Q7 The diagram below shows an **X-ray tube**.

a) Name and describe the process by which the filament releases electrons into the X-ray tube.

....

....

Hot filament (cathode)   Lead casing   Evacuated glass tube

X-rays   Anode (metal target)

b) Each electron released is accelerated by a potential difference of 55 kV. Calculate the kinetic energy gained by each electron.

....

....

Use charge on an electron = 1.6×10^{-19}.

c) X-rays used in **fluoroscopy** are produced using X-ray tubes.

The patient is placed between the X-ray tube and a fluorescent screen.
Briefly describe how the **fluorescent screen** is used to produce a live **image** of inside the body.

....

....

....

....

Particles in Atoms

Q1 Alpha, beta and gamma are all types of ionising radiation, but they have quite different properties.

a) Rate the different types of radiation according to their penetrating power.

> 1 = high penetrating power
> 2 = moderate penetrating power
> 3 = low penetrating power

alpha ☐   beta ☐   gamma ☐

b) How does the **penetrating power** of each type of radiation compare to its **ionising power**?

....

c) Give an example of a material that can stop

i) alpha radiation ....   **ii) beta** radiation ....

Q2 Indicate whether the following statements are **true** or **false**.

	True	False
a) A positron is a positively charged neutron.	☐	☐
b) The number of protons in atom is equal to the number of electrons.	☐	☐
c) Positrons, electrons and neutrons all have the same relative mass.	☐	☐
d) The relative charge on a proton is +1.	☐	☐
e) Positrons have the same ionising and penetration properties as an electron.	☐	☐

Q3 Neutrons are found in the nuclei of atoms and can also be emitted as a form of radiation. Underline the correct words from the options given.

a) Neutron radiation is **more / less** penetrating than alpha or beta radiation.

b) Neutrons do not have electric **charge / power** so they do not directly **absorb / ionise** material they pass through.

c) Absorbing a neutron can make a nucleus **ionised / radioactive**.

Q4 Shielding made of **concrete** can be used as protection against neutron radiation.

a) Explain how the shielding works.

....

b) Concrete shielding alone is not enough to prevent the harmful effects of neutron radiation. Explain why.

....

....

c) Write down an example of a material that could be added to the shielding to stop any radiation getting through. ....

Stability and Radioactive Decay

Q1 Complete each of the sentences about **radioactive decay** by choosing the correct words or numbers from the list below each one. You may use some words more than once.

a) During α decay, the nucleus loses .... protons and .... neutrons.

So its nucleon number decreases by .... and its proton number decreases by ....

1   2   3   4

b) During β⁻ decay a .... becomes a .... The proton

number increases by 1 and the nucleon number ....

stays the same   proton   neutron   electron   increases

c) During β⁺ decay a .... becomes a .... The proton

number .... and the nucleon number stays the same.

proton   increases by 1   stays the same   neutron   decreases by 1

d) α, β⁺ or β⁻ decay results in the formation of a different ...., which is shown

by the change in .... number.

element   nucleon   proton

e) When a nucleus emits a γ ray, its mass number changes by .... and its proton

number changes by ....

0   1   2   4

Q2 The equation shows an isotope of carbon undergoing radioactive decay.

a) What type of radioactive decay is this?

....

$$^{14}_{6}C \longrightarrow X + {}^{0}_{+1}e$$

b) Give the **nucleon number** and **proton number** of element X.

nucleon number: ....

proton number: ....

Decaying sock
⚠ incinerator ⚠

c) People take precautions against cell damage from ionisation by most types of radiation. Why is it not necessary to take particular precautions against this type of radiation?

....

Top Tips: A β⁺ decay here, a β⁻ decay there. This all might seem a tad confusing, but it's important to get your head around what becomes what, e.g. a neutron turning into a proton etc. Make sure you know how the proton and nucleon numbers are affected by α, β⁺ or β⁻ decay too.

Stability and Radioactive Decay

Q3 The graph on the right shows the number of neutrons (N) against the number of protons (Z) for **stable isotopes**.

a) What are **isotopes** of an element?

....

....

b) Are isotopes in region A stable or unstable? Circle your answer.

     stable   unstable

c) Are isotopes in region A neutron-rich or proton-rich?

     neutron-rich   proton-rich

d) Suggest a reason why isotopes in region B are **unstable**.

....

e) In order to achieve stability, what type of decay will isotopes in **region B** undergo?

....

f) What type of decay will isotopes in **region C** undergo in order to achieve stability?

....

g) What type of particle will isotopes in **region D** emit in order to become more stable?

....

Q4 **Alpha particles** are strongly ionising.

a) What kinds of atom undergo alpha decay?

....

b) Circle the two of these elements that undergo alpha decay.

       H   **U**   **Th**   **C**   **He**

c) Complete this nuclear equation.

$$^{224}_{88}\text{Ra} \longrightarrow \boxed{}\text{Rn} + \boxed{}\text{alpha}$$

d) After alpha (or beta) decay, a nucleus often has too much energy. How does it lose this energy?

....

Quarks

Q1 Tick the statements that are **true**.

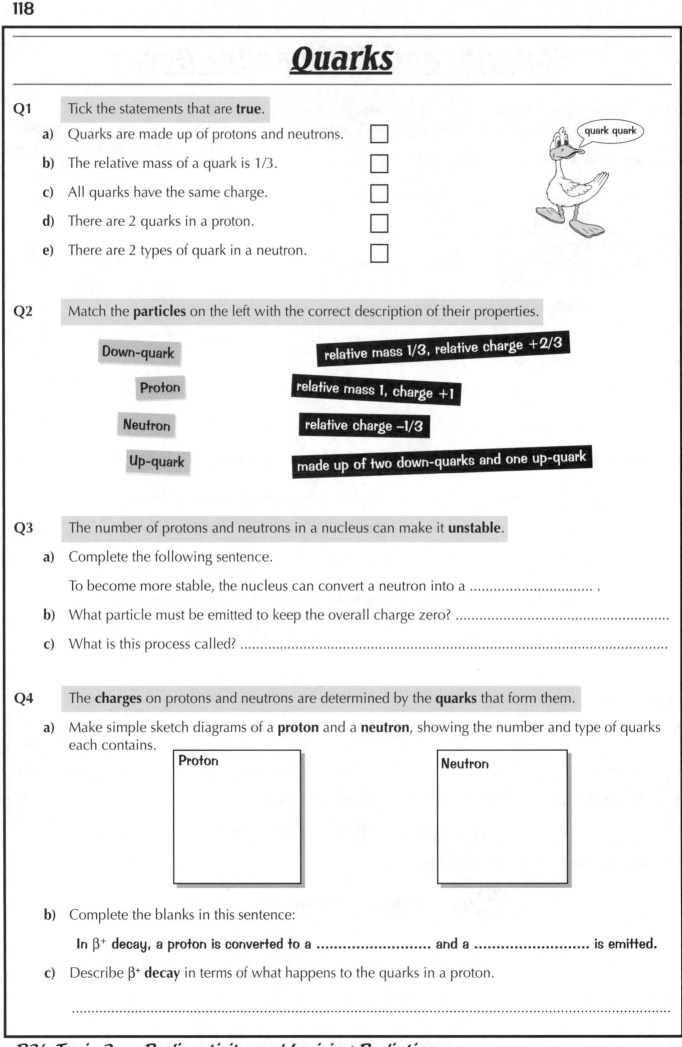

a) Quarks are made up of protons and neutrons. ☐

b) The relative mass of a quark is 1/3. ☐

c) All quarks have the same charge. ☐

d) There are 2 quarks in a proton. ☐

e) There are 2 types of quark in a neutron. ☐

quark quark

Q2 Match the **particles** on the left with the correct description of their properties.

Down-quark

Proton

Neutron

Up-quark

relative mass 1/3, relative charge +2/3

relative mass 1, charge +1

relative charge –1/3

made up of two down-quarks and one up-quark

Q3 The number of protons and neutrons in a nucleus can make it **unstable**.

a) Complete the following sentence.

To become more stable, the nucleus can convert a neutron into a ....

b) What particle must be emitted to keep the overall charge zero? ....

c) What is this process called? ....

Q4 The **charges** on protons and neutrons are determined by the **quarks** that form them.

a) Make simple sketch diagrams of a **proton** and a **neutron**, showing the number and type of quarks each contains.

Proton	Neutron

b) Complete the blanks in this sentence:

In β⁺ **decay, a proton is converted to a** .... **and a** .... **is emitted.**

c) Describe β⁺ **decay** in terms of what happens to the quarks in a proton.

....

Medical Uses of Radiation

Q1 **Positron emission tomography** (PET) is a scanning technique used in hospitals.

a) Give one advantage and one disadvantage of PET compared to X-rays.

i) advantage: ....

ii) disadvantage: ....

b) Give two conditions that can be diagnosed using PET.

....

Q2 Put the following stages in the right order to explain how PET is carried out.

☐ The tracer moves through the body to the organs.

☐ Detectors around the body record the position of the emitted gamma rays.

☐ The patient is injected with the tracer.

☐ The positrons collide with electrons and are annihilated, releasing gamma rays.

☐ The radioisotope emits positrons.

1 A positron-emitting radioactive isotope is added to a substance used by the body to make a tracer.

☐ A computer builds up a map of radioactivity in the body.

Q3 The **map of radioactivity** in the body produced by a PET scan can be used to detect active cancer tumours.

a) i) What does the map of radioactivity match up with?

....

ii) Why is this?

....

b) Explain why a PET scan is a good way to detect cancer.

....

c) Why is PET not used frequently on the same patient?

....

Q4 **Radiation exposure** can be damaging, but is also used as a medical treatment.

a) Explain how radiotherapy can be used as a form of **palliative care**.

....

....

b) Describe **two** ways that radiation can damage cells.

....

Medical Uses of Radiation

Q5 A hospital has recently installed a new PET scanner and a cyclotron to produce the isotopes needed.

a) Explain why the isotopes used in PET scanners have to be produced nearby.

....

....

b) The medical personnel using the equipment must take precautions to limit their exposure to ionising radiation. Write down **two** precautions they could take to minimise their exposure.

1. ....

2. ....

Q6 Radiation can be used **internally** and **externally** to treat tumours.

a) What is internal radiation therapy?

....

b) Give **one** advantage of internal radiation therapy over the use of external sources of radiation.

....

c) Describe **one** advantage of using external treatments instead of internal radiation therapy.

....

....

Q7 Imagine a **new** technique using **radiation** has been developed to treat breast cancer. It has been tested on people with end-stage breast cancer, and shown to be an effective treatment with tolerable side effects.

a) The technique has not been tested on people with early-stage breast cancer.

i) Why might someone with early-stage breast cancer want to receive treatment using this new technique?

....

ii) Suggest why doctors would be unwilling to give this new treatment to patients with early-stage breast cancer.

....

b) There are many **ethical** issues associated with the use of radiotherapy. Outline one such issue.

....

....

Cyclotrons

Q1   A **satellite** orbiting the Earth travels at a constant speed.

a)   Is the satellite accelerating? Explain your answer.

....

b)   Put a tick next to each true statement below.

☐   "If a body is accelerating then there must be a resultant force acting on it."

☐   "The forces acting on a body going round in a circle at a steady speed must be balanced."

☐   "If there is no resultant force acting on a body then it carries on moving in a straight line at the same speed."

c)   What is the general name for a force that keeps a body moving in a circular path?

....

Q2   Choose from the words given below to complete the passage.

curved	magnetic	spirals	lose	perpendicular

A charged particle in a .... field will experience a force. The force is always

.... to its direction of travel — so the particle follows a ....

path. If only a magnetic field is present, the particles will move in ....

rather than circles because they .... energy and slow down as they

interact with other particles.

Q3   A cyclotron is a type of **particle accelerator**. The diagram to the right shows the path of a charged particle in a cyclotron.

The charged particle starts at the centre of the cyclotron.

a)   Describe the path of the particle as it moves through the cyclotron.

....

b)   Explain why the particle follows the path described in part **a)**.

....

....

....

....

Two hollow semicircular electrodes

Path of charged particle

Magnetic field perpendicular to the page

Alternating potential difference

Particle leaves cyclotron

Think about the energy of the particles and what the magnetic field is used for.

122

Uses of Particle Accelerators

Q1 Bombarding stable elements with **protons** can produce **radioactive isotopes**. Complete the following passage using some of the words provided.

nucleus	accelerator	cyclotron	electron	proton	element	mass

A proton is absorbed by the .... This increases its

.... number so a new .... is produced.

The proton needs a lot of energy before it can be absorbed by the nucleus, so this process

takes place in a particle .... called a ....

Q2 The radioactive isotopes produced by proton bombardment are **unstable**.

a) Complete the following equations to show how two radioactive isotopes are formed.

$$^{18}_{8}O + ^{1}_{1}p \longrightarrow \boxed{}F + ^{1}_{0}n \qquad ^{14}_{7}N + ^{1}_{1}p \longrightarrow \boxed{}C + ^{4}_{2}He$$

b) i) What sort of radiation do the radioactive isotopes formed in this way usually emit?

....

ii) Suggest a medical use for these radioactive isotopes.

....

Q3 Scientists at CERN use an enormous **particle accelerator** to smash particles into each other at tremendous speeds.

a) Explain how particle accelerators can help scientists gain a better understanding about the Universe.

....

....

....

b) Give two reasons why scientists from all over Europe collaborate on the research at CERN.

....

....

....

....

Alan and the guys hadn't realised collaborative working meant one computer between five.

Top Tips: Proton bombardment — that sounds pretty scary. But it's actually really useful. Cyclotrons are used to bombard protons at stable isotopes to create radioactive isotopes for use in medicine. Oh Mr Proton Bombardment, you're not so scary after all. I'm sorry I ever doubted you.

Momentum and Kinetic Energy

Q1 The diagram shows a fast moving **neutron colliding** with a stationary sodium **nucleus** and bouncing off again.

Before   **After**

m_n m_s m_n m_s

V_1 $V_2 = 0$ V_3 V_4

  a) Using the notation in the diagram, write an expression for:

  i) the total momentum before the collision.

  ....

  ii) the total momentum after the collision.

  ....

  b) Using your answers to part **a)**, explain what is meant by the term **conservation of momentum**.

  ....

Q2 The diagram shows the **alpha decay** of **uranium-238**.

Use the relative masses in your calculations.

$^{238}_{92}U \longrightarrow {}^{4}_{2}He + {}^{234}_{90}Th$

  a) i) Add an arrow to the diagram to show which way the **thorium** nucleus will move.

  ii) Explain why it must move this way.

  $v = 0$ km/s $v = -15$ km/s

  ....

  ....

  b) Calculate the **velocity** of the thorium nucleus immediately after the decay.

  ....

Q3 Tick the boxes to show the properties **conserved** in an:

KE   **Momentum**

  a) elastic collision.   ☐   ☐

  b) inelastic collision.   ☐   ☐

Strawberry = conserved.

Q4 A 1 kg ball moving at a velocity of 4 m/s collides with a stationary ball of mass of 3 kg. After the collision, both balls move off in opposite directions.

Before   **After**

1 kg   3 kg   1 kg   3 kg

$v = 4$ m/s $v = 0$ $v = -2$ m/s $v = 2$ m/s

  a) Calculate the total kinetic energy before the collision.

  ....

  ....

  b) Was kinetic energy conserved in the collision? Show your working.

  ....

  ....

Momentum and Kinetic Energy

Q5   The diagram below shows the **collision** of a neutron and an atom of uranium-235.

$^{1}_{0}n$ $^{235}_{92}U$

$\overrightarrow{v = 2 \text{ km/s}}$ $\overrightarrow{v = 0.1 \text{ km/s}}$

a)   Calculate the relative momentum of the:

i)   neutron. ....

ii)   uranium-235 nucleus. ....

b)   The uranium-235 nucleus absorbs the neutron to form uranium-236.

i)   What is the relative momentum of the uranium-236 isotope?

....

ii)   Calculate the velocity of the uranium-236 isotope.

....

c)   Was the collision elastic or inelastic? Show your working.

....

....

....

Q6   Kobe is testing two bouncy balls. He wants to find out which ball is the bounciest.
He drops both balls from a height of **100 cm** onto a wooden floor. He records their
rebound heights for three subsequent bounces. His results are shown in the table below.

a)   Name the type of energy the balls have
just before they're dropped.

....

b)   Which ball was the bounciest?

....

	Ball 1	Ball 2
Height of 1st bounce (cm)	63	76
Height of 2nd bounce (cm)	45	55
Height of 3rd bounce (cm)	22	31

c)   Explain why the balls never reach the same height as their previous bounce.

....

....

d)   Suggest **one** factor Kobe could change to alter the rebound heights of the balls.

....

Top Tips: If you know your equations, this topic is the chance to earn some tasty marks
without too much trouble. Learning equations isn't the most exciting job in the world — but it does
pay off. Remember, things with momentum are **mo**v**ing** — and that momentum equation — m × v.

Annihilation and PET Scans

Q1 The diagram represents the **collision** of an **electron** and a **positron**.

electron positron

e⁻ e⁺

→ ←

a) What happens when a particle collides with its antiparticle?

....

b) The electron and positron are travelling at the same speed before the collision. What is the value of their **total momentum** immediately before the collision?

....

c) Choose the correct words from each pair to complete the sentences below.

The collision of an electron and a positron produces a pair of **gamma rays / radioactive particles**. The **gamma rays / radioactive particles** produced have the same **energy / velocity** as each other, and opposite **energies / velocities**.

d) What is the value of the **total momentum** immediately after the collision? Explain your answer.

....

e) Read the statement below.

"Charge isn't conserved in a positron and electron annihilation, because the total charge after is zero."

Do you agree with the statement? Explain your answer.

....

....

f) Explain how this collision is an example of mass energy conservation.

....

g) Calculate the minimum energy released when an electron and positron collide. The mass of an electron/positron is 9.1×10^{-31} kg and the speed of light is 3×10^8 m/s.

....

....

Q2 Below is a diagram showing a patient undergoing a **PET scan**. Before the scan, the patient was injected with a **positron-emitting radio isotope**.

Use the diagram to help you explain how the radio isotope is used in PET scanning.

....

....

....

....

....

Kinetic Theory and Absolute Zero

Q1   Tick the correct boxes below to show whether the sentences are true or false.   **True False**

a)   The particles in a **liquid** are free to move at **high** speeds.   ☐ ☐

b)   The particles in a gas have **more** energy than those in liquids and solids.   ☐ ☐

c)   In a solid, the particles can only **vibrate** about a fixed position.   ☐ ☐

d)   In a liquid, the particles form **irregular** arrangements.   ☐ ☐

e)   The particles in a liquid have **less** energy than those in a solid.   ☐ ☐

Q2   Complete the following paragraph by choosing words from the box below.

0 °C	ice	0 K	100 °C	–273 °C	absolute	water

The Celsius temperature scale has two fixed points. One is the melting point

of .... at .... The other is the boiling point

of .... at .... The lowest fixed point on the

Kelvin temperature scale is at the lowest temperature possible — called

.... zero. This is given a value of .... and it is

equivalent to a temperature on the Celsius scale of about ....

Q3   Convert the following temperatures to **kelvin** (K).

a)   3 °C   ....

b)   210 °C   ....

c)   –45 °C   ....

d)   0 °C   ....

Q4   Convert the following temperatures to **°C**.

a)   0 K   ....

b)   300 K   ....

c)   640 K   ....

d)   30 K   ....

Q5   Explain, in terms of the **movement of particles**, why there is a theoretical absolute zero temperature.

....

....

....

Pressure, Volume and Temperature of Gases

Q1   Complete the following sentences by choosing the correct word(s) from each pair.

a) When a gas is heated, the particles in it move **faster** / **more slowly**.

b) The average **kinetic** / **potential** energy of particles in a gas is **equal** / **proportional** to the temperature of the gas on the kelvin scale.

c) For a gas at a constant pressure, the volume is **proportional** / **inversely proportional** to temperature.

Q2   **Kinetic theory** can be used to explain the behaviour and properties of gases.

a) What does kinetic theory say that a gas consists of? Circle **two** of the options A to E below.

     A stationary particles   **B** very small particles   **C** a rigid mesh of particles

     D mostly empty space   **E** fluctuations in electric and magnetic fields

b) Explain how the impact of gas molecules on the sides of a container relates to the pressure of a gas.

....

....

Q3   The kinetic energy of particles depends on their **mass** and their **velocity**.

a) What is the **formula** for the kinetic energy of a particle of mass **m** travelling at velocity **v**?

....

b) The temperature of a gas is increased from 277 °C to 827 °C. At 277 °C the mean kinetic energy of the gas is 1.14×10^{20} joules. What is it at 827 °C?

Always start a kinetic theory question involving temperature by converting degrees Celsius to kelvin.

....

....

c) Explain why it takes longer for the smell of air freshener to spread through a room on a cold day than on a hot day.

....

Q4   A bag of elephant trump is kept in a sealed bag at **300 K**. The bag is carelessly left on a radiator. The gas heats up to a temperature of **345 K** and the volume expands to **0.575 m³**. Calculate the initial volume of the gas if the pressure remains constant.

....

....

....

....

Pressure, Volume and Temperature of Gases

Q5 Ruth is using a **gas syringe** to investigate **ideal gas laws**. In her first experiment, she investigates the relationship between **volume** and **temperature**.

a) Use words from the box to complete the description of the experiment below. You may not need some of the words.

outwards	expand	inwards	air	contracts
increases	volume	Bunsen burner		pressure

The gas syringe is half filled with .... and sealed with a rubber bung.

The syringe plunger is free to move, allowing the gas to be kept at a constant

.... A .... is used to heat the gas, causing it to

.... The syringe plunger is observed to move ....

as the gas is heated. When the gas cools back down again, the plunger moves

back to its original position because the gas .... as it cools.

This shows volume .... as temperature of the gas increases.

b) Describe an experiment Ruth could do using a pressure sensor with the gas syringe to investigate the relationship between pressure and volume. Say what this experiment would show.

....

....

....

....

Q6 The gas in the container on the right has an initial volume of **0.65 m³** and an initial pressure of **101 325 Pa**.

a) Calculate the pressure of the gas if the volume is reduced to **0.45 m³** and the temperature remains constant

....

....

b) Explain, in terms of **particle collisions**, the reason for the change in pressure you calculated in part **a)**.

....

....

....

Gas Pressure and Medicine

Q1 A bubble of carbon dioxide leaves a plant at the bottom of a lake. Initially it has a volume of **5 cm³** and is at a pressure of **607 950 Pa**. The temperature at the bottom of the lake is **4 °C**. The bubble rises and just before it reaches the surface it is at a pressure of **101 325 Pa** and a temperature of **20 °C**.

a) Give two reasons why the volume of the bubble will **increase** as it rises.

1. ....

2. ....

b) Calculate the **volume** of the bubble just before it reaches the surface.

Don't forget to convert temperatures to kelvin.

....

....

....

Q2 Gases are often used in **hospitals**, where they have to be kept in **pressurised canisters**.

a) Give **two** reasons why hospitals store gases in canisters at pressures higher than atmospheric pressure.

1. ....

2. ....

b) A **1750 cm³** canister stores nitrogen gas at a temperature of **300 K** and a pressure of **8 atm**. The pressure outside the canister is **1 atm** and the temperature is **300 K**.

Remember that pressure can be measured in Pa or atm. If both the initial and final pressures are in atm, there's no need to convert to Pa.

i) What is the maximum volume of nitrogen that can be released from the canister?

....

....

....

ii) The canister is fitted with a valve that controls its flow rate. Calculate how long it will take the canister to release the volume of gas you calculated in part **b) i)**, in minutes, if the flow rate is **5 cm³** per second.

....

....

Top Tips: Don't let questions with lots of different values phase you — it's really just a matter of figuring out which equation to use and plugging in the numbers. In gas canister questions, remember that the canister will never empty completely — the gas stops flowing when the pressures inside and outside the canister are equal, so some gas will always be left behind.

Mixed Questions — P3b Topics 3, 4 & 5

Q1 When **high-energy** electrons are fired at protons and neutrons the deflection of the electrons shows that both protons and neutrons are made up of charged particles called **quarks**.

a) Describe the types of quark found in protons and neutrons, include their relative charge and mass.

i) up-quarks: ....

ii) down-quarks: ....

b) Write down the quark configuration of a proton.

....

Q2 Anna is investigating the properties of stable and unstable isotopes. She fires neutrons at a stable isotope of carbon. The isotope **absorbs a neutron** and becomes unstable. Anna adds the unstable isotope to a graph showing the number of neutrons against the number of protons in stable isotopes.

a) Would you expect the unstable carbon isotope to lie above, below or on the line of stability on the graph? Give a reason for your answer.

....

b) **i)** Complete the following equation describing the decay of the isotope: $^{13}_{6}C \longrightarrow \boxed{}\,N + ^{0}_{-1}e$

ii) What is this sort of decay called? ....

c) Describe the decay in terms of what happens to the **quarks** in a neutron within the isotope's nucleus.

....

d) The isotope is still unstable because it has too much **energy**. How can the isotope become stable?

....

Q3 A container of ideal gas has a pressure of **1×10^5 Pa** and a volume of **100 cm³**.

a) The volume of the gas is gradually increased while the temperature remains constant. Calculate the **pressure** of the gas at the following volumes.

i) 200 cm³ ....

ii) 400 cm³ ....

b) When the pressure of the gas is 1.25×10^4 Pa, what will its **volume** be?

....

....

c) On the grid opposite, draw a **graph** showing how pressure varies against volume at constant temperature for this gas.

<u>Mixed Questions — P3b Topics 3, 4 & 5</u>

Q4 An atom of nitrogen is bombarded with **proton radiation** in a cyclotron.

a) Why does this process need to take place in a cyclotron?

....

b) The nitrogen nucleus absorbs a proton. Why does this result in a new **element**?

....

c) The new element formed is an unstable isotope of carbon.
What sort of radiation would you expect it to emit?

....

Q5 One of Dr McLeod's patients has cancer and is being treated with **radiotherapy**.

a) What sort of radiation would be used in this treatment?

....

b) Dr McLeod thinks that the radiotherapy won't cure his patient's cancer,
but will reduce her suffering. What type of care is this? ....

c) Dr McLeod hears about a new drug that might help his patient. The drug has not yet been
tested on cancer patients and the company is looking for volunteers to take part in a trial.
Outline an argument for and against this patient taking part in the trial.

For: ....

....

Against: ....

....

Q6 A **hydrogen atom** travels at a velocity of **300 m/s** when it collides elastically with
a helium atom travelling in the **opposite direction** at a velocity of **–200 m/s**.

a) What **two** properties are conserved in an elastic collision?

....

b) The hydrogen atom leaves the collision with a **final velocity** of **–400 m/s**.
Calculate the **final velocity** of the helium atom.

You'll need to use the
relative atomic masses
for helium and hydrogen.

....

....

....

P3b Topic 5 — Kinetic Theory and Gases

Mixed Questions — P3b Topics 3, 4 & 5

Q7   The gas inside a rigid, **sealed** container is cooled from 527 °C to –73 °C.

a)   Convert these temperatures to kelvin:

i) 527 °C = ... K   **ii)** –73 °C = ... K

b)   State whether each of the following will increase or decrease with the temperature change:

i) the average **kinetic energy** of the gas particles: ....

ii) the average **speed** of the gas particles: ....

iii) the average **force** exerted on the walls of the container: ....

Q8   Mary has epilepsy. She is having a **PET scan** of her brain as part of a research study.
Before the PET scan, Mary is given an injection of a radio isotope.

a)   Describe what happens to the **positrons** emitted by the radioisotope in Mary's brain.

....

b)   Explain how **momentum** is **conserved** in this process.

....

....

....

Q9   Radon gas is a source of background radiation that occurs naturally in the air.

a)   The following incomplete equation shows $^{222}_{86}\text{Rn}$ ➡ ▢ Po + ▢ ....
the decay of radon gas to solid polonium.

i) What sort of decay would you expect radon to undergo? Give a reason for your answer.

....

ii) Complete the equation.

b)   A balloon full of radon gas of volume **0.02 m³** at a pressure of **101 kPa** is heated from **273 K** to **293K**.
The balloon expands to **0.025 m³**. Calculate the pressure at the new temperature and volume.
Assume the radon behaves as an ideal gas.

....

....

....